D1478594

THE THEORY OF ELEMENTARY WAVES

A NEW EXPLANATION OF FUNDAMENTAL PHYSICS

LEWIS E. LITTLE

New Classics Library

The Theory of Elementary Waves

A New Explanation of

Fundamental Physics

Printed in the United States of America

For information, address the publishers:

New Classics Library
Post Office Box 1618
Gainesville, Georgia 30503 USA
Phone: 800-336-1618, 770-536-0309
Fax: 770-536-2514
Web site: www.newclassicslibrary.com

New Classics Library is the book publishing division of
Elliott Wave International, Inc.

ISBN: 978-0-932750-84-6
Library of Congress Catalog Number: 2009920400

"You believe in a dice-playing God and I in perfect laws in the world of things existing as real objects."

—Albert Einstein

Acknowledgments

I wish to thank several individuals who have contributed significantly toward the writing of this book and toward the development of the ideas it contains:

First and foremost, I thank physicist Stephen Speicher, who for ten years championed the Theory of Elementary Waves and helped to promote it, frequently doing more in the latter regard than I did myself. During those ten years he served as a sounding board for my ideas, offering frequent helpful criticisms and suggestions. It is tragic that Stephen is no longer with us to witness the publication of the work to which he contributed so significantly. I have dedicated this work to his memory in expression of my appreciation for all he has done.

I also thank Dr. Frank Schneider for his help for eight or more years in promoting the theory, for inviting me to speak about the theory at Jet Propulsion Labs, and for reading the manuscript in several versions while I was writing it, offering helpful criticisms and advice.

I must thank Bob Prechter for his painstaking editing of the book, also in more than one version, and for enduring endless debates with me regarding passive voice and other issues. I am especially indebted to him for his recognition of the value of the Elementary Wave Theory and the importance that this work be written and published. I thank also Mr. Prechter's entire publication staff, and in particular Sally Webb for her meticulous attention to detail in the book's presentation.

I thank Dr. Naomi Sarna for inspiring me to write a book for non-physicists. Although not a physicist herself, her insatiable curiosity led her to read the famous *Feynman Lectures* on physics. Her comments regarding the double-slit experiment and the notion of a particle going through both slits gave me the idea to introduce the Elementary Wave Theory in the manner of Chapters 2 and 3. It is to Dr. Sarna and to all similarly curious and thinking individuals that I address this work.

—Lewis E. Little

Table of Contents

Foreword

My favorite books are ones that dispel decades, centuries or millennia of misconception in one brilliant stroke. Intricate, long-standing theories built upon such misconceptions are called "error pyramids." Perhaps the greatest error pyramid ever constructed in the hard sciences was the one built around the false premise of a geocentric universe. Some planets appeared to act weirdly as a result of this error, such as Mercury moving "retrograde" with respect to Earth. Astronomers produced complicated calculations and theories to account for the motion of the planets in a perceived geocentric solar system, even to the point of perfect prediction. Yet Copernicus' 1543 book on celestial mechanics, *On the Revolution of the Heavenly Spheres*, wiped away the entire vision and replaced it with one that made sense not only in the calculations but also, for the first time, in the physics.

This is precisely Lewis Little's achievement with respect to the behavior of sub-atomic particles: making the physics fit the calculations. When I read his obscure paper on the Theory of Elementary Waves, I knew he had a vision as revolutionary as that of Copernicus 350 years earlier. I arranged to meet Little in New York and offered to publish his book, whenever he wrote it. It is a pleasure to see that day finally arrive.

For me, the journey to this book has been not only intellectual but also personal. In college, I abandoned two majors in succession—physics and economics—because I refused to waste my time on what appeared to be flawed ideas. Errors permeate economics, and although they are profound, they are mostly pedestrian; in physics the matter is quite different: Quantum mechanics embraces absurdity. It proposes, for example, that a subatomic particle has multiple identities simultaneously when no one is watching but condenses into a single identity when an observer looks at it. Werner Heisenberg, who described quantum mechanics in 1925, formulated in 1927 what has come to be called the "uncertainty principle" or "principle of indeterminacy," by which he postulated, "The 'path' [of a subatomic particle] comes into existence only when we observe it."[1] An observer's consciousness, QM theoreti-

---

[1] Heisenberg, "The actual content of quantum theoretical kinematics and mechanics," Zeitschrift fuer Phys. (West Germany), v. 43, no. 3-4, 1927 p 172-198.

cians insisted, can bring an object into actuality. "Bell's theorem," they said more recently, "refutes reality." People who espoused this nonsense would look at you with a mischievous grin, as if they were supremely clever and your skepticism was sad ignorance. I could not imagine pursuing such ideas as my life's work.

What's Wrong with Twentieth Century Quantum Mechanics

Scientists have accurately observed the patterns of sub-atomic particle emission and diffusion, yet they have come to bizarre conclusions about the universe as a result. Here is a highly simplified version of the situation: Sub-atomic particles travel by waves, but they do not appear to behave as one would initially expect. The famous "double-slit" experiment shows that when a source shoots particles toward a barrier into which two narrow slits have been cut, the particles that travel through the slits create a distribution pattern on the surface of a detecting screen on the other side of the barrier. The pattern indicates that waves determine the trajectory of the particles. Fine. But then when the experimenter shifts the position of the screen, the new distribution pattern indicates that particles are taking different trajectories after passing through the slits. In other words, changing the location of the screen alters the trajectory of particles along the waves that carry them. Physicists have had extreme difficulty explaining this phenomenon. How can the location of the detector screen, where we merely observe the distribution pattern, affect the motion of the particles before they arrive there?

Quantum physicists boldly propose that reality itself changes to accommodate the observer. They attempt to describe waves and sub-atomic particles not as things but as mere co-existing potentials—"wave-particles"—that follow all paths corresponding to all possible detector locations simultaneously as long as they are unobserved. These non-entities "collapse" into actuality only upon being observed, the very act of which literally creates an actual particle. Bingo. The mere act of looking turns an unexplained (and inexplicable) potential into an entity, which shows up at the detector one is using.

The uncertainty principle, which most physicists have accepted since its formulation, states that accurate measurement of quantum behavior is impossible in principle because the very existence of subatomic particles depends upon the action or non-action of an observer. In other words, the simple act of observing particles alters reality, making it impossible to detect and measure any sub-atomic system without disrupting the system and thus altering the measurements. Our mental powers of reality alteration, which operate whether we want them to or not, thereby present an insurmountable impediment to knowing reality, because there is no constant reality to know. The inescapable further conclusion is that there is no direct causality from one physical event to the next; it all depends upon consciousness, which in turn determines the ultimate paths of particles, backwards in time.

Quantum physicists do not satisfactorily explain how sub-atomic particles would behave were there no conscious beings to observe them. They do not explain how consciousness can remain constant when its domicile—a brain—is constructed of unobserved, non-actual potentialities. But the problem goes even deeper than that. If there is no constant reality, what is a detector? What is a particle? What are you? What is your mind? None of these things has definition absent actuality. You cannot even discuss your metaphysical philosophy when you hold this belief, because no one can trust your words to mean anything.

It takes an intellectual to recognize the fundamental error in a theory with self-contained impossibilities and to challenge it on principle. Albert Einstein knew that the conclusions of quantum mechanics were wrong because, as he put it, "You believe in a dice-playing God and I in perfect laws in the world of things existing as real objects." In other words, consistent physical reality and causality are universal principles. He diplomatically stated his opinion that quantum mechanics was therefore "incomplete."[2]

You can imagine the intellectual gymnastics required (Einstein happily excepted) to maintain a concoction as contradictory as quantum mechanics. As George Orwell, an astute observer of the human mind, once observed, "There are some ideas so wrong that only a very intelligent person could believe in them."[3] Indeed, Richard Feynman

___

[2] Einstein, Albert, Fifth Solvay International Conference on Electrons and Photons, October 1927, Brussels.

[3] Gleick, James, *Genius—The Life and Science of Richard Feynman*, Pantheon, New York, 1992, front flap.

by all accounts was—as his biographer calls him—a Genius. If a certi-fied genius can formulate the "famous notion of antiparticles traveling backward in time,"[4] which is incorrect, then what do we call the man who finally gets it right?

Lewis E. Little Clears Up the Mystery of Quantum Mechanics

It is not so much that Lewis Little has an I.Q. north of 200, which he does. Many individuals have a high I.Q. What matters is how it's applied.

From the beginning, physicist Lewis E. Little thought properly about the problem of explaining sub-atomic behavior because, like Einstein, he knew that the conventional explanation is contradictory, which means that it is wrong. He did not wonder if it was wrong; he knew it was wrong, for the same reasons that one cannot properly "wonder" about ghosts, which (by most attempts at definitions) are inexpressible as a concept. A ghost is impossibly defined as simultane-ously an entity and a non-entity—corporeal and non-corporeal, actual and non-actual—at the same time, just as a so-called "wave-particle" is defined today. Conventional attempts to explain quantum mechanics, Little observes, are equally fundamentally flawed: "Proofs claiming that one couldn't avoid contradictions didn't prove that those contradictions were real. They rather proved that the premises of those proofs already contained a contradiction." As you can see, Little is less courteous than Einstein, preferring accuracy when no less than reason and reality are at stake.

Recognizing the fundamentally erroneous nature of quantum mechanics is available to philosophers and logicians, but it takes a theo-retical physicist to discern the source of the error in QM's description of the physics involved in sub-atomic behavior. It then takes an especially creative mind to take the next step and solve the problem with an alter-native depiction of the objects and behavior involved.

Understanding the essential error of thought led Little to look for a purely physical explanation of sub-atomic behavior, an explanation that did not rely on ghosts, backwards time and psychokinesis. He began by

---

[4] Gleick, James, *Genius—The Life and Science of Richard Feynman*, Pantheon, New York, 1992, front flap

recognizing that there must be a physical explanation for the fact that the placement of the detector affects the path of the sub-atomic particles. This is an entirely different thing from saying that observation, much less consciousness, determines particles' very existence. By looking for a physical cause rather than acquiescing to those who would modify the metaphysics of reality, Little's mind paved the way for a solution.

In this book, Little exposes 20th-century quantum mechanics as the second-biggest error pyramid ever constructed in the hard sciences; then he takes a deep breath and blows it over with one mighty puff. Little's thesis presents a new theory that places activity at the sub-atomic level on the same grounds of cause and effect as all other physics. To reach this understanding, he has to challenge one of quantum physicists' bedrock premises—a pure, unexamined assumption of physical behavior—which the evidence, properly applied, refutes. In the end, he not only revolutionizes the fundamentals of sub-atomic physics but also reclaims the fundamentals of scientific philosophy.

Though Little is certain that the essentials of his theory are correct, he does not claim to have covered every possible detail. He does, however, resolutely maintain two overriding points: (1) The very fact that he can formulate a purely physical theory of observed sub-atomic behavior refutes quantum mechanics' assertion that only compromised reality and time-reversed cause-and-effect can explain that behavior. (2) The Theory of Elementary Waves is consistent with all evidence of behavior at the sub-atomic level, including the phenomenon of relativity. Whether Little has found the truth behind sub-atomic behavior only time and more knowledge will tell. No one at this stage can insist that it is the only possible explanation. But until a better one comes along, Lewis Little's Theory of Elementary Waves is the only theory of sub-atomic behavior that can properly demand our attention.

—Robert R. Prechter, Jr.

THE THEORY OF
ELEMENTARY WAVES

Chapter 1

INTRODUCTION

The science of physics, as conceived by today's leading academic theoreticians, has become insane to the point of farce. Physicists proudly claim to have demonstrated that subatomic particles can be in two different places at the same time; that time can go backwards; that widely separated events can affect one another instantaneously and by no means; that the effect of an action can precede its cause; that objects can exist whose physical parameters have no quantitative value in particular and/or many different values simultaneously; that many behaviors of subatomic particles occur by chance and are uncaused; that the law of cause and effect has been refuted; that there are multiple universes, indeed an infinite number of universes; that these universes are filled with "dark matter," more aptly termed "ghost matter"; that the entire universe arose from an object the size of a pinhead; that the object exploded in a "big bang" to give us the universe we live in today; that subatomic particles are actually 11-dimensional "strings"; that the universe is "left-handed"; and other absurdities too numerous to list. An internationally known physicist and professor at Cornell has stated, "We now know that the moon is demonstrably not there when nobody looks."[1] And yes, he was dead serious. It is as if physics, once a science whose purpose was to render the physical universe intelligible, had morphed into the exact opposite: an absurdist drama based on the theme that we live in a universe where nothing makes sense, exhorting people to abandon reason altogether.

---

[1] N. David Mermin, *The Journal of Philosophy*, Vol. **78**, No. 7 (July, 1981), pp. 397-408.

The truth is, all of this "modern physics" is exactly what it appears to be: total nonsense. Some 80 or 90 years ago, physicists made a fundamental error in their development of the theory known as quantum mechanics, the bedrock theory of modern subatomic physics. Because the theory is erroneous, physicists inevitably began to uncover laboratory evidence that contradicted it. In the face of that evidence, physicists should have retraced their steps until they discovered the error; but instead, reluctant to give up the partial success they had achieved with the theory, they chose to "twist" reality in an attempt to make it agree with the theory. The absurdities listed above are the product of that twisting. As physicists uncover more and more contradictory evidence, they do more and more twisting, with the absurdities becoming ever more preposterous with each new experiment. Today, matters have reached the ultimate extreme: Serious academics, publishing in the leading physics journals in the world, claim to have "refuted reality," by which they mean that physical behaviors are not the product of anything real. The title of an April 20, 2007 article appearing on physicsweb.org and reporting on a paper that appeared in the scientific magazine *Nature*, reads: "Quantum physics says goodbye to reality."[2]

On the contrary, reality has for many years been saying an increasingly pointed goodbye to quantum mechanics. Discovery of the correct theory of subatomic phenomena, providing an understanding of the reality we see and not a twisted version thereof, is long overdue. This volume presents—and substantially validates—the Theory of Elementary Waves (TEW), a theory that accounts for the facts without resorting to magic.

TEW presents a transparently accessible picture of subatomic phenomena. One could successfully teach the basic concepts to 8th graders. Nonetheless, the theory explains—not merely describes, but explains—everything allegedly accounted for by quantum mechanics, and more. Quantum mechanics, along with much of modern physics, riddled as it is with contradictions, undefined terms, disembodied behavior and other "weird" notions that defy reason, has given many observers the impression that physics is by nature an incomprehensible science. Indeed, many modern physicists appear intent upon making the

---

[2] physicsweb, "Quantum physics says goodbye to reality," 20 April, 2007

subject as opaque as possible, having built their public reputations largely around their alleged ability to comprehend the incomprehensible. As this volume will demonstrate, however, even subatomic physics, when correctly explained, is quite straightforward.

Chapter 2 takes the matter directly to the fundamental experiments, beginning with the very basic "double-slit" experiment. This is the paradigm experiment of quantum mechanics; it captures the entire "problem" of quantum mechanics. The chapter explains how the supporters of quantum mechanics come to the conclusion that it is impossible, even in principle, to explain this experiment. They assert that the experiment compels one to accept contradictions—or what many physicists evasively term "quantum weirdness"—and to incorporate these contradictions into quantum mechanics. The chapter examines two further key experiments that point in the direction of the correct explanation. Chapter 3 then takes the results of the latter two experiments, puts two and two together, and shows how these results lead directly to a coherent, non-contradictory explanation of the double-slit experiment.

The very fact that a non-contradictory explanation of the findings of the double-slit experiment can be conceived of at all, even if merely hypothetically, demolishes the basic arguments used to justify quantum mechanics—the arguments allegedly proving that it is impossible to explain this experiment in a non-contradictory manner. The supporters of quantum mechanics maintain that such an explanation is impossible in principle, yet this work explicitly presents just such an explanation.

The remainder of Chapter 3 extends the explanation of the double-slit experiment to subatomic phenomena more generally. Chapters 4 through 6 describe further experiments that allegedly demonstrate "quantum weirdness" and show how TEW explains these experiments in a non-contradictory manner. Included is a rebuttal of Heisenberg's so-called "uncertainty principle."

Chapter 7 demonstrates that TEW, with no further assumptions or embellishments, provides a physical explanation of Einstein's theory of relativity. The otherwise strange phenomena predicted by that theory, including the apparent slowing down of rapidly moving clocks and the apparent shortening of rapidly moving objects, become physically transparent.

The fact that TEW explains relativity theory provides substantial corroboration that TEW is in fact the correct theory of subatomic phenomena. The real test of any proposed theory is not that it merely account for the subject phenomena but that it also make additional predictions that are confirmed in the laboratory. Had Einstein or another physicist not as yet discovered relativity, TEW would have predicted it; and, of course, experiment would then have shown the prediction to be correct.

To be sure that there is no misunderstanding, TEW does not purport to overturn relativity theory, if by relativity theory one means Einstein's basic equations relating what each of two observers sees when one observer is in motion relative to the other. On the contrary, TEW explains why those equations are true. To use technical terms (defined later), TEW explains why it is that space and time are "Lorentzian" and not "Galilean." TEW presents a very different physical picture of relativity—and, by the way, a picture much closer to what Einstein himself believed would have to be the case. TEW eliminates, among other things, the notion that space is some sort of real "stuff" that expands and shrinks as implied by the modern approach to the theory.

TEW does not attempt to explain subatomic phenomena by appeal to the laws of "classical physics": Newton's laws of motion, momentum conservation, energy conservation, etc.—"billiard ball" physics, so to speak. On the contrary, TEW explains why these classical laws are true—true, that is, in describing the behavior of macroscopic objects. The explanation, presented in Chapter 9, suggests a profoundly different view of the physics surrounding the classical concepts of mass, momentum and energy. Based on similar considerations, Chapter 10 proposes a new, entirely picturable physical explanation of magnetism.

The absurdities of modern physics go well beyond those contained in quantum mechanics proper. Chapter 11 describes a few theories of modern physics that are either vacuous or so lacking in scientific evidence as to be little better than mystical fantasies. Considered in particular are the theories of "parity violation" and "dark matter," as well as the attempts by physicists to achieve what they term "grand unification." An alternative approach to the phenomena falsely attributed to parity violation leads directly to a clear physical picture of the nature of so-called "anti-matter."

Chapter 12 describes the TEW picture of the atom. Atomic decay, according to quantum mechanics, occurs in large part by chance between atomic levels of "uncertain" energy. According to TEW, decay occurs as the result of causal interactions between real objects always existing in a single, definite state. Chapter 13 discusses some possible future applications and expansions of TEW.

Modern physicists conceive of physics not as a science dealing with the nature of real entities and their consequent behavior but instead as nothing more than a mathematical description of behavior. According to this view, explanations have no place in physics. While the philosophies held by modern physicists are probably as numerous as the physicists themselves, what they have in common is what might most charitably be characterized as the view that real objects are constituted by the behavior they exhibit—that behavior is, in effect, the ultimate constituent of the universe. This behavioral approach has led physicists further and further away from reality. The present volume will demonstrate the enormous strides that we can make in discovering the nature of our universe merely by remembering one very simple and obvious principle: Behavior is always behavior of *something*—something real.

Chapter 2

QUANTUM MECHANICS

2.1 The Double-Slit Experiment

The study of atomic and subatomic physics began in the late 19th and early 20th centuries, the first major step being physicist J. J. Thomson's discovery of the electron in 1897. In the years immediately following, physicists discovered, through a variety of experiments, that the physical laws known up until that time—the so-called "classical" laws of physics—could not account for the behaviors of subatomic particles. They discovered that the behaviors were governed not by Newtonian mechanics but by waves. Thus began the development of the theory known today as quantum mechanics.

As theory and experiment developed further, physicists began to question more than merely the physics of the classical era. They began to question the basic principles underlying the scientific Enlightenment, including even the principle that real entities exist and are what they are independent of our looking at them. The view that we live in a universe of real objects obeying exact and intelligible laws began to break down.

One experiment in particular, the so-called double-slit experiment, illustrates all of these developments: the wave-like behavior of particles, the fact that classical physics could not account for this behavior, and the apparent need to reject an objective reality. Many physicists consider this to be the paradigm experiment of quantum mechanics. Richard Feynman, in particular, has stated that the double-slit experiment captures the entire "problem" of quantum mechanics.[1]

---

[1] R.P. Feynman, *Proceedings from the Second Berkeley Symposium on Mathematical Statistics and Probability*, University of California Press, Berkeley (1951).

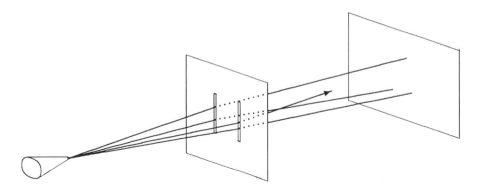

Figure 2.1: Double-Slit Experiment

The double-slit experiment is pictured in Figure 2.1. A source on the left fires subatomic particles toward a barrier into which two parallel slits have been cut. The barrier stops all particles except those penetrating the slits. The latter particles travel to a screen on the right, where their points of impact are recorded. After many particles have reached the screen, the experimenter observes the pattern formed by the impacts.

If the particles obeyed the laws of classical physics, then after penetrating a slit they would simply continue traveling on a straight line over to the screen—the same straight line that they had been following prior to arriving at the slit. After many particles penetrated the slits, the pattern on the screen would then look like Figure 2.2, in effect simply a negative image of the slits. If the slits were particularly narrow, particles might scatter somewhat randomly off the edges of the slits, superposing on Figure 2.2 a fairly uniform pattern of particle impacts over the entire width of the screen.

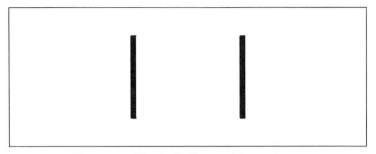

Figure 2.2: Classically Expected Screen Image

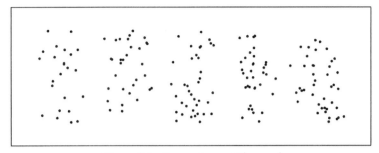

Figure 2.3: Screen Image Observed

What experimenters have actually found, however, is a pattern similar to that shown in Figure 2.3: a wavy pattern showing an alternation between areas where many particles arrive and areas where few particles arrive. Clearly Figure 2.3 looks nothing like Figure 2.2, with or without a superposed uniform pattern.

The pattern observed looks very much like the pattern that would be produced if the source, instead of emitting particles, were instead emitting waves. Figure 2.4 illustrates how waves can form such a pattern. Imagine that the figure is depicting water waves, viewed from above looking down. The various lines represent the crests of the waves. The dark, wide line represents a barrier having two small openings. Waves are entering from the top of the figure. The barrier absorbs any waves

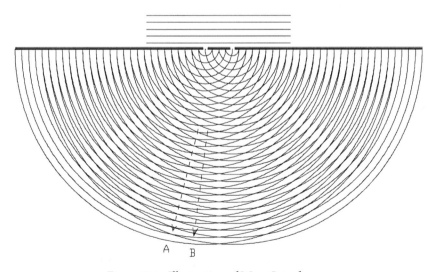

Figure 2.4: Illustration of Wave Interference

that impact it directly. At the openings, however, the water oscillates up and down as the waves arrive. This oscillation generates new waves on the downward side of the barrier, emanating from each of the openings. Those waves spread out radially, as depicted by the semi-circular lines centered on each opening.

For the simplest kind of wave motion—wave motion that physicists describe as being "simple harmonic"—it turns out that the waves from the two openings propagate independently from one another; the height of the water at any particular location and time in the presence of both waves is the simple sum of the heights that would be produced by each wave in the absence of the other. Along a direction such as that toward point A in the figure, the crests of the two waves arrive together, as do the valleys between crests. The two waves are then said to be exactly "in phase" with one another. They combine to produce a roughly double-size wave. The height of the waves—the "amplitude"—is large at point A. Along a direction such as that toward point B, the crest of one wave arrives at the same time as the valley between crests for the other wave. The two waves are exactly "out of phase" with one another. As a result, the two waves cancel each other out; little or no wave arrives at B—the "amplitude" is roughly zero at B.

At points between A and B there is some degree of cancellation and some degree of addition. At points close to A, the waves largely reinforce each other, leaving a large amplitude, though not as large as at point A. At points close to B the waves largely cancel each other, leaving a small amplitude. Scanning along the line from A to B, the amplitude gradually shifts from the large amplitude at A to the small amplitude at B. As one continues around the circle, the amplitude shifts back and forth between large and small. The overall pattern is termed an "interference pattern" produced by the "interference" of the two waves.

The pattern formed in the double-slit experiment, as shown in Figure 2.3, looks very much like such an interference pattern. Quantitatively, in fact, the pattern observed in the experiment is identical to a wave interference pattern. Physicists concluded that the particle source generates some sort of wave, which then penetrates the two slits, and the resulting wavelets coming from the slits then interfere with one another and produce the observed pattern.

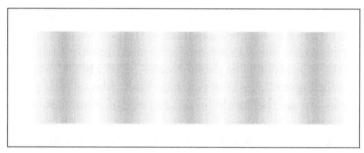

Figure 2.5: Pattern with Direct Wave Interaction

While the pattern of the particle impacts in Figure 2.3 does look like a wave interference pattern, the figure differs in one important respect from what two interfering waves would directly produce. Compare Figure 2.3 with Figure 2.5. Figure 2.5 illustrates the pattern of the intensities of two interfering waves when those waves interact directly with whatever device records the intensities. The pattern varies smoothly and continuously throughout, while Figure 2.3 consists of individual "dots." The pattern in Figure 2.3 shows up as the result of the impact of numerous individual particles.[2]

We must therefore not overlook a crucial fact: The experimenter in the double-slit experiment does not observe the wave directly. He observes the "dots"—the locations of the particle impacts—directly, and then infers the wave from the pattern of the dots. Most physicists openly agree that the wave is not observed directly, but they then have amnesia on this point when carrying out their further analyses of the experiment.

The fact is, the hypothesis that a wave from the particle source accounts for the observed pattern is exactly that: a hypothesis. The evidence supporting this hypothesis, from this experiment and many others, appears to be overwhelming. But we must remember that this explanation of the pattern is hypothetical.

The hypothesis that waves from a particle source are responsible for the behavior of the particles emitted from that source constitutes the es-

---

[2] After a sufficiently large number of particles have arrived at the screen, Figure 2.3 may end up looking like Figure 2.5; but the pattern consists nonetheless of the points of impact of numerous individual particles.

sence of quantum mechanics.[3] More generally, the hypothesis maintains that a wave moving in the same direction as the forward motion of a subatomic particle governs the behavior of the particle. This hypothesis will hereafter be referred to as the "forward-wave hypothesis."

Modern physicists do not recognize this hypothesis as constituting the essence of quantum mechanics because they assume it to be self-evident and not a hypothesis at all.

2.2 Apparent "Weirdness"

Once physicists concluded that a wave emitted by the particle source explains the pattern, they then proceeded with an attempt to explain the paths of the individual particles. This is where the trouble began.

If the wave is ultimately the cause of the pattern, but it is the arrangement of particle impacts on the screen that actually reveals that pattern, then the particles must somehow be "following" the wave—or so it would seem. The problem with this picture is that the pattern on the screen isn't formed because the waves merely arrive there. It is specifically interference between the waves from the two slits that (allegedly) produces the pattern. That interference is produced by waves moving along multiple paths from slits to screen, not merely along any one path that a particle might follow. In any ordinary theory, a particle would be affected only by the waves making actual contact with the particle. Because the particle takes only one path—or so one would think—and the waves along that one path cannot by themselves produce the pattern, there is no way those same waves could cause the particle to move in such a way as to reflect the pattern.

More specifically, waves moving along the two straight lines, one from each slit, to a particular point on the screen produce, at least in part, the interference at that point. The two straight lines meet only at the screen. In no way could the waves along both lines simultaneously affect a particle's motion prior to its arrival at the screen—or, again, so one would think.

---

[3] In some formulations of quantum mechanics a wave from the particle source does not appear explicitly, but the formulations are nonetheless physically equivalent.

Figure 2.4 might make it appear as if the waves could cause a particle to move along a "channel" such as that along the line ending at point A. But the figure is, in this respect, misleading. At all points between the slits and the screen, whether within a "channel" or not, the wave from each slit would act independently on a particle. Each wave propagates independently, as indicated in the previous section. It is only at the screen that the two independent waves actually meld together to produce the interference pattern.

Indeed, this latter fact captures the essence of the whole problem with this picture of a particle following a forward wave. The alleged interference pattern produced by the wave—not per se the pattern revealed by the particle impacts, but the actual physical phenomenon constituting the alleged interference pattern produced specifically by the wave—exists only at the screen. Yet somehow that physical phenomenon must guide a particle's motion before the particle arrives at the screen. How could this be?

One manner in which modern physicists have attempted to circumvent these difficulties is to postulate instantaneous "action at a distance," or, to use their more recent term, "nonlocality." They maintain that a particle's motion is affected not merely by interaction with the wave in the "local" environment of the particle, but in addition through a "nonlocal" interaction between the particle and every portion of the wave (or its physical equivalent) throughout its entire extent in the greater environment of the particle. Equations employing this nonlocality have been made to "work"—to relate a particle's motion to objects in the environment in such a manner as to reproduce the observed pattern.

Instantaneous action at a distance is, however, a contradiction in terms. An action of one object on another can take place only by some real physical means. Something has to travel from the acting object to the object affected in order to produce the effect. Instantaneous action over a distance would imply an action carried out by no means. But if there is no means, there is no action. Instantaneous action at a distance would also contradict the well-established laws of Einstein's theory of relativity, which maintains that nothing can travel faster than the speed of light.

Appeal to an alleged nonlocal interaction explains absolutely nothing. It is merely a fancy, scientific sounding way to claim that the phenomenon in question is inexplicable. It "just happens"—for no reason.

Whether from the double slit experiment or others, the overwhelming majority of modern physicists maintain that nonlocality is a well established physical fact.

An earlier and more "standard" means by which physicists have tried to account for the behavior of the individual particles, in the double-slit experiment and elsewhere, is to postulate that the wave and the particle are not separate entities at all but that what exists instead are "wave-particles." These wave-particles are waves while travelling from particle source to screen, but instantly "collapse" into particles upon arrival at the screen.

This picture entails almost too many contradictions to list. To begin with, a particle is by definition a sharply localized object; a wave is necessarily a widely extended object. The very term "wave-particle" is a self-contradiction. When the wave "collapses" into a particle at a particular point on the screen, the entire wave must join that instantaneous collapse. Otherwise two separate portions of the wave might each transform into a particle before either transformation could affect the other. One particle would then magically become two. An instantaneous "collapse" would thus necessarily involve an instantaneous, nonlocal interaction of each portion of the wave with every other portion.

Based on the "wave-particle" and other similar pictures, the overwhelming majority of modern physicists will insist that the particle does not go through one slit or the other but instead goes through both slits.

In addition to the nonlocal interaction and the "wave-particle" approaches, physicists have proposed a medley of what they refer to as "interpretations" of quantum mechanics. Every interpretation, however, leads to contradictions. Furthermore, physicists have offered alleged proofs that no theory free of contradictions—free of "weirdness"—could possibly, even in principle, account for the behavior of the individual particles. Physicists claim to have proved thereby that we have no choice but to embrace the contradictions in one "interpretation" or another, and, in particular, have no choice but to embrace nonlocality. They even claim that nonlocality has been directly exhibited in a famous experiment performed at Innsbruck, Austria, frequently referred to as "the Innsbruck experiment."

Observe that both of the interpretations considered above assume that the wave originates from the particle source—that it is a forward-moving wave. In the nonlocality interpretation, the particle follows the forward-wave "nonlocally;" in the "wave-particle" interpretation, the forward-wave somehow "is" the particle. All of the proposed interpretations of quantum mechanics, and all of the alleged proofs that contradictions are unavoidable, though different from one another in many other respects, are based, explicitly or implicitly, on this same assumption. Physicists have not proved that no theory free of contradictions can explain the double-slit experiment. What they have proved is that no theory based on the forward-wave hypothesis can explain the double-slit in a non-contradictory manner. Given that the forward-wave hypothesis is a hypothesis, not an observed fact, and given that, based on that hypothesis, it is impossible to explain without contradiction (this being a redundancy) part of what is observed, what must a reasonable person conclude?

After all, the particles do arrive at the screen. They don't get there by magic. The fact that they get to the screen proves that they had some real means of doing so, and therefore that their behavior can, at least in principle, be explained, without contradiction—without anything having to be what it isn't. The "weirdness" proofs offered by physicists do not prove that contradictions exist. The contradictions prove that the forward-wave hypothesis is false.

Contradictions do not exist in reality. A non-means of transmission cannot be a means. A widely extended object cannot be a non-extended object. Any real object or physical process—any real phenomenon of any sort whatsoever—can be only what it is, not what it isn't. A is A.

Physicists have introduced the notion of an "interpretation" of quantum mechanics in response to the appearance of these allegedly irresolvable contradictions. They insist that the equations describing the forward wave must be correct because they "work," meaning that the equations correctly predict the observed pattern. The question then, they maintain, is how to "interpret" those equations—translation: how to incorporate the contradictions into the theory in the most palatable manner. This, of course, is little more than an exercise in rationalization. Nonetheless, physicists have proposed numerous "interpretations," written many hundreds of papers and dozens of books, held international conferences, created entire schools of thought involving new systems of philosophy around their own chosen interpretation and put more thought into this issue than perhaps has been put into any other issue in the history of physical science—all as the result of a mistake: acceptance of the forward-wave hypothesis.

If a theory correctly identifies what exists, or even if it merely proposes what might exist, on what possible basis could it require "interpretation"? If all one has is a formula that "works," on what possible basis could it be termed a "theory"?

Modern physicists claim to be interested only in developing formulas that "work" in describing behavior. Contradictions are of no concern to them; after all, they are merely developing a formalism, not describing anything real. Contradictions, in this view, manifest a new, "higher" logic within this extra-real formalism. Once they have developed their formalism, however, they contradict themselves by claiming that their formalism establishes facts about reality, such as the claims that the particle goes through both slits and that nonlocality exists. Perhaps the best name for their methodology would be the "somersault philosophy."

The English words "particle," "two," "places," "nonlocal," etc., after all, do refer to reality. There is nothing else to which they might refer. If they don't refer to anything real, then they are noises or empty scribblings, not words. When physicists make their "weirdness" claims, the general public certainly understands their words as being words with a meaning. If their words are not intended to mean anything, then physicists are obligated to say so, and the public would then be able to draw the appropriate conclusion.

The alleged proofs of the existence of contradictions by the advocates of quantum mechanics are negative in nature. Physicists have not proved directly that illogical phenomena—phenomena involving contradictions—actually exist. They instead allege to have proved that the double-slit and other similar experiments cannot possibly be ex-plained in a logical manner and are therefore inexplicable in principle. A single counterexample would thus totally destroy those alleged proofs, and quantum mechanics along with them.

Of course, any alleged proof of the existence of contradictions is self-nullifying anyway. Logical proof assumes the validity of the law of non-contradiction. The usefulness of logic in the development of our knowledge of reality—and there is nothing else to know—requires that the law of non-contradiction be true in reality. Were it not true—if con-tradictions could exist—proofs of any kind would be vacuous. Indeed, the very concept of proof would be meaningless. What would a proof be proving if the opposite to its conclusion could be true as well?

The following sections describe two more experiments that reveal different, but equally challenging, problems with quantum mechanics. As with the double-slit experiment, the results, viewed objectively, simultaneously point the way to a proper solution.

2.3 Time Goes Backward?

In 1992, H. Kaiser et al. published the results of an experiment that they claimed exhibited backward-in-time causation.[4] The experiment is illustrated in Figure 2.6. A particle source on the left (not shown in the figure) fires neutrons into an interferometer. The neutrons pass through the three thin crystalline plates making up the interferometer, numbered 1, 2, and 3 in the figure. The first plate deflects some of the neutrons into the upper path through the interferometer, while other neutrons pass straight through the first plate and take the lower path. The middle plate deflects the two paths back together at the third plate. A sample of bismuth placed in the upper path slows down the neutrons taking that path. The third crystal then deflects the neutrons onto one or the other of the two paths leaving the interferometer.

In the first part of the experiment, the analyzer crystal shown in the figure is absent. In its absence, slowly increasing the thickness of the bismuth is found to cause the neutrons, upon leaving the third crystal, to switch back and forth between deflecting in the direction toward one detector and the direction toward the other. At one thick-

---

[4] H. Kaiser, R. Clothier, and S. A. Werner, Phys. Rev. A **45**, p. 31 (1992).

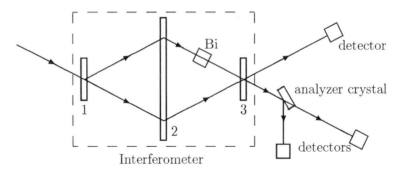

Figure 2.6: Experiment of Kaiser et al.

ness of the bismuth, all of the neutrons appear at the detector at the top. As one gradually adds more bismuth, some of the neutrons begin to appear at the lower detector and fewer at the upper. With enough additional bismuth, all of the neutrons appear at the lower detector. As one continues to add still more bismuth, the particles gradually switch back to the upper detector; they continue switching back and forth in this manner as more and more bismuth is added.

Modern physicists account for the switching by assuming that a wave from the neutron source is taking the two paths through the interferometer—much like the wave going through two slits in the double-slit experiment—producing interference between the waves when they meet at the third crystal. The bismuth slows down the wave in the upper path, so the peaks and valleys of that wave arrive at the third crystal later than they otherwise would. This delay alters the interference with the wave from the lower path, thus causing the combined wave to deflect differently. When the waves arrive at the third crystal in phase with each other, they deflect one way; when out of phase, the other.

In the second part of the experiment, the experimenter continues to add still more bismuth until at some point the interference stops; the individual neutrons go randomly toward one detector or the other regardless of the addition of any further bismuth. Modern physicists account for this result by asserting that the wave corresponding to a single neutron is actually a "wave-packet"—a little "burst" of wave having a relatively short length. The little packet divides and takes both paths through the interferometer—so the "neutron" is now two places at once—with interference occurring when the two packets come back together at the third crystal. But if the bismuth slows down the packet in the upper path sufficiently, the two packets will no longer overlap when they arrive at the third crystal. The packet on the lower path will already have passed through the crystal before the packet on the upper path arrives. There will thus be no interference.

There is still another part to the experiment: Even with enough bismuth to stop the interference, if the experimenter now inserts the analyzer crystal shown in Figure 2.6, the interference returns. When particles deflect downward upon leaving the interferometer, they arrive at the analyzer crystal, which deflects some of them further downward to the third detector. When particles deflect upward upon leaving the interferometer, none of them arrive at the third detector. As the experimenter gradually adds still more bismuth, the arrival of neutrons at the third detector switches on and off, thereby demonstrating that the interference has returned—demonstrating, that is, that the neutrons are again switching back and forth between deflecting up and deflecting down upon leaving the interferometer.

The effect of the analyzer is to reduce what physicists term the "bandwidth" of the waves. The interferometer is designed to pass waves of one particular frequency, but it will actually transmit waves of a small range or "bandwidth" of frequencies around that particular frequency. The analyzer acts to narrow the bandwidth further; it reflects only a small "sub-bandwidth" of the waves that have passed through the interferometer.

According to quantum mechanics, narrowing the bandwidth will increase the length of the wave packets corresponding to the neutrons. The longer packets will then again overlap at the third crystal even when the shorter packets didn't. This is the alleged reason why the interference returns upon inserting the analyzer.

But observe: If the waves involved were moving in the same direction as the neutrons—if they were forward waves—the action of the analyzer would not affect the waves until after they had already passed through the interferometer. How could the interaction with the analyzer crystal possibly affect what had already taken place in the interferometer? Incredibly, modern physicists, still unwilling to abandon quantum mechanics, have concluded that the action of the analyzer crystal alters what occurs in the interferometer...backward in time! They claim that this experiment directly demonstrates the existence of "reverse-temporal causation." And again, as with the Cornell professor who claims that the moon doesn't exist when nobody is looking at it, this is not some kind of whimsical joke. They are dead serious.[5]

Were the experimenter to insert the analyzer crystal after a "wave-particle" had already traversed the interferometer, the prediction of quantum mechanics would nonetheless remain the same. So, the wave-packets are one length—call it "short"—when they go through the interferometer; but no, they weren't short; they were "long," as effectuated by the analyzer when the particles arrive there. As the wave-particles traverse the interferometer, they are both short and long and neither and both—if one believes quantum mechanics. The absurdity is manifest.

Time cannot go backward. Time is the measure of motion. The direction of a motion can be reversed, but doing so would not reverse time. Time can only go forward. If time could go backward, we would be unable to determine which way anything went. One sees a car driving down the street. It appears to be moving forward. Nope; that car is backing up, backward in time. The notion of time going backward is truly insane, to the point of farce.

Some physicists maintain that Einstein's "general" theory of relativity predicts the possibility of traveling backward in time. If this conclusion were a necessary consequence of Einstein's theory, it would not confirm the possibility of backward-in-time phenomena. On the contrary, it would constitute an iron-clad refutation of Einstein's general theory of relativity.

In this experiment, as in the double-slit, it is the assumption that the particle is following a wave (or "is" a wave) coming from the particle source that "forces" one to accept the weirdness—the backward in time causation. So again, given that the forward-wave hypothesis is a hypothesis, and given that it leads to the absurd notion of reverse-time causation, what must a reasonable person conclude?

If whenever evidence contradicts a theory it were valid simply to invent some new contradiction and declare it to be real, any theory

---

[5] Kaiser et. al., op. cit.

could be made to "work." Such an approach is the utter antithesis of the scientific method. A scientist, properly so-called, takes reality as the given. Implicit in this approach is the abstract principle that A is A. After all, what would this "given" reality be—what "reality" would one be talking about—if any object or phenomenon might just as well be something else? Part and parcel with the acceptance of reality is the rejection of contradictions.

Many of the same modern physicists who postulate reverse-temporal causation to account for the results of the Kaiser experiment maintain at the same time that the law of cause and effect has been refuted. They object to any proposed causal explanation of any phenomenon but then turn around and maintain, at least by implication, that the law of cause and effect is valid whenever they need it to justify their preposterous conclusions. It is tempting to conclude that these physicists actually have no issue with the law of cause and effect, just so long as the causes propounded make no sense.

2.4 Atomic Emission in a Resonant Cavity

Physicists can cause an electron in an atom to jump to a higher or "excited" energy level by, for example, shining light of the appropriate frequency on the atom. If a particle of that light—called a photon—is absorbed by the atom, it will supply the energy needed to produce the jump. Having achieved this state of excitation, the electron will subsequently drop back down, or "decay," to a lower level and emit a photon in the process. If the atom is in free space, unaffected by objects in its environment, the decay will occur in a characteristic time, determined by the nature of the atom and its excitation.

Physicists have performed experiments in which they place an atom inside a very tiny square "box" with walls that reflect light—a so-called "resonant cavity." When they then excite the atom to a higher energy level, it usually decays much more slowly than it would in free space. In some particular instances, the atom decays much more rapidly than in free space.

As with all subatomic particles, a wave governs the behavior of a photon. According to quantum mechanics, because the atom emits

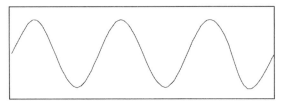

Figure 2.7: Wave of 3 Wavelengths that "Fits"

the photon particle, the atom also emits the photon wave. Depending on the "interpretation" of quantum mechanics being employed, the wave is emitted either with or as the photon. Inside a resonant cavity, an atom will freely emit a photon—this again according to quantum mechanics—only if the emitted wave "fits" in the cavity. A wave "fits," according to this theory, only if the length of a dimension of the cavity is exactly equal to an integral multiple of the wavelength of the wave. An example of a wave that "fits" is illustrated in Figure 2.7, in which the width of the box is exactly equal to 3 wavelengths of the wave. When any such wave travels across the cavity, reflects and comes back, and then reflects and travels across again, the resulting twice-reflected wave will be exactly in phase with the wave when it made the first trip across; the wave reinforces itself upon multiple reflection. On the other hand, if the width of the cavity is not equal to an integral multiple of the wavelength, the multiply-reflected waves will be out of phase to some degree, both with the initial wave and with each other, and upon multiple reflections the wave will cancel itself out. In this case the wave doesn't "fit."

In most instances—for most cavities into which an atom might be placed—the wave doesn't fit, so the decay doesn't occur or occurs much more slowly. For the special case where the wave does fit, the multiple reflections greatly reinforce the wave, and the decay occurs more rapidly.

But quantum mechanics has a serious problem: If the wave comes from the atom, how does the atom "know" whether or not the wave will fit until it has already emitted the wave? What happens if the wave is emitted and then finds that it doesn't fit? (A modern physicist might say that the wave un-emits itself backward in time!)

Quantum mechanics attempts to avoid this obvious contradiction by inventing the notion of "available states." The atom will emit only if the appropriate available state—a "place" where the wave might go—is present in the cavity to accommodate the emission; and only available states that fit in the box are "available." Presumably these available states reflect back and forth in the cavity to establish their availability or unavailability.

But this explanation merely compounds the absurdity. An available state is not a thing; it is the "place" where a thing—a real wave—might go. By itself it is nothing, and nothing cannot accommodate an emission or reflect back and forth and interfere with itself or do anything else. Nothing is nothing. This is an overt instance of abandoning reality—of alleging that nothing can exist and do something. Quantum mechanics would virtually have us believe in ghosts.

In all three experiments discussed in this chapter, the laboratory evidence clearly refutes the forward-wave hypothesis and quantum mechanics along with it. The attempts to salvage quantum mechanics with "nonlocality," "backward time" and "available states" are simply too preposterous to be taken seriously.

Chapter 3

THE THEORY OF ELEMENTARY WAVES

3.1 The Essence of TEW

While the arguments in Chapter 2 make clear that quantum mechanics is seriously flawed, the experimental evidence supporting the theory appears nonetheless to be overwhelming. In the double slit experiment, the pattern formed on the screen by the particle impacts is—but for the fact that it consists of individual "dots"—exactly the pattern that would be formed by a wave originating at the particle source. Physicists have found this to be true of the patterns formed in virtually all subatomic particle experiments performed to date. Yet Chapter 2 has demonstrated that a forward wave could not possibly be the cause of these patterns. How can this be?

The Kaiser experiment, described in Section 2.3, provides the clue. This experiment does not demonstrate that time goes backward. What it demonstrates is that the wave that the neutrons follow is moving in the direction opposite to that postulated by quantum mechanics—in the direction opposite to the motion of the particles. The fact that the presence of the analyzer crystal changes the behavior of the wave in the interferometer proves that something is moving from the analyzer crystal to the interferometer to produce the change. The wave and the particle are the only moving objects involved; there is no evidence of the presence of any third object. The particle clearly moves from the interferometer to the analyzer; otherwise the particle would not arrive at the detector. The only object that could be moving in the reverse direction is the wave.

Quantum mechanics has the waves moving in the wrong direction. This is the "fundamental error" referred to in the second paragraph of Chapter 1.

But, according to quantum mechanics, the wave is emitted with (or as) the particle and thus appears on the scene only at the very moment when the particle "needs it." If the wave moves in reverse, how does it come about that the wave is present precisely when "needed?" The resonant-cavity experiment, described in Section 2.4, provides the answer to this and several further questions. The experiment clearly shows that waves looking very much like the so-called "available states" do exist in the cavity. A particle photon can be emitted only in response to the stimulation of a wave of the appropriate wavelength. Only the waves that "fit" have sufficient intensity to provide this stimulation; the waves that don't fit have little or no intensity as the result of self-interference. (The latter waves are still present but have little or no effect on the emission of photons.) These waves are, of course, real physical waves, not just "available states" for waves. In order that they be able to do anything, they first have to exist. The wave that stimulates the atom's emission of a photon does not come from the atom—it is not a "forward wave" that is then placed into an "available state." It is a wave already present in the cavity prior to the photon's emission.

In general, particles are emitted only in response to the stimulation of an already existing wave and with a probability proportional to the intensity of that wave. When a particle travels from a source at point A to a detector at point B, it does so by following a wave that emanates from the detector at point B. The wave propagates out from point B, scatters through whatever physical objects exist between A and B, and some intensity of the wave arrives at the particle source at point A. The wave at point A stimulates the emission of the particle, and the particle then follows the wave back to the detector at point B. The wave emanating from the detector at point B is present at all times, not only at the time when the source emits a particle at point A.

A great deal of experimental evidence confirms the existence of these waves—waves that are real objects in their own right, separate from particles. So intent are modern physicists in retaining the forward-wave theory, however, they fail to recognize that their "available states" are real waves. They construct a fictitious wave-particle out of the wave-like behavior of particles and simultaneously fail to recognize the existence of the waves that actually do exist.

The remainder of this presentation will demonstrate, among other things, that TEW makes exactly the same prediction as quantum mechanics for the probability that a particle emitted at point A will arrive at point B. This is true for any object or system of objects with which the particle interacts between points A and B. TEW explains what occurs, however, in a manner free from the contradictions that plague quantum mechanics.

In keeping with the usual terminology of physicists, from this point on I will refer to the reverse-moving wave as the "reciprocal wave." The reason for this terminological choice will become clear as we proceed.

3.2 The Double-Slit Revisited

Figure 3.1 provides an abstract representation of the double-slit experiment. As in Figure 2.1, the source on the left emits particles, some of which penetrate the two slits and impact the screen on the right. The wavy line drawn to the right of the screen represents the pattern formed by the particle impacts.

The figure also depicts the two paths that a particle might follow in traveling from the source to a particular point P on the screen, with each path traversing one slit. For the particular point P chosen in the figure, the upper path is somewhat longer than the lower. One way of visualizing the difference in path length is indicated in the figure. Clearly the path difference will change as one moves point P across the screen.

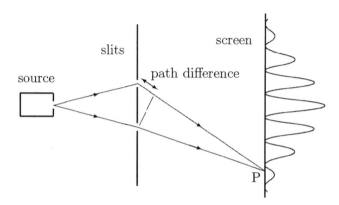

Figure 3.1: Double slit path difference analysis

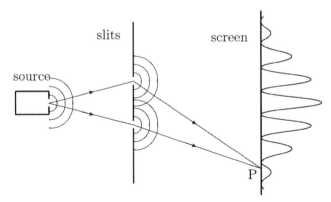

Figure 3.2: Quantum mechanical wave picture

In the quantum mechanical picture, shown in Figure 3.2, the wave is coming from the particle source. It propagates in all directions to the right of the source, and in particular along the lines of the two particle paths. The oscillations in each slit then generate wavelets to the right of each slit. They propagate in all directions from each slit, and again along the lines of the two particle paths.

Because the lengths of the two paths are different, the wave along the longer path will lag behind the one on the shorter path, resulting in interference at point P. Suppose the wavelength of the wave were such that the sum of, say, 3 wavelengths exactly equaled the length of the path difference. In that case, even though the wave along the upper path would be 3 wavelengths behind the other, the two waves would end up exactly in phase with each other upon arriving at P. Maximum wave intensity at P would be the result. If for some other point P only 2.5 wavelengths would fit in the path difference, the two waves would end up exactly out of phase with one another at the screen and the result would be a minimum in wave intensity. One thus sees how interference between the waves will produce a pattern that oscillates between maximum and minimum as one scans along the screen, just as in Figure 2.4.

Quantum mechanics says that the probability of observing a particle at point P is proportional to the intensity of the forward wave at point P. But in fact, when a particle follows a wave, the motion of the wave is in the direction opposite to that of the particle. In the double-slit experiment, the wave that affects a particle's motion emanates from the screen. In the case of a particle that travels to point P, the wave be-

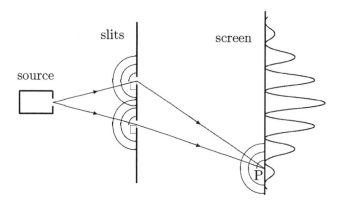

Figure 3.3: Reverse wave double slit experiment

ing followed emanates from point P. This pre-existing, reciprocal wave propagates in all directions to the left of point P, as shown in Figure 3.3, and in particular along the two particle paths. It penetrates the two slits—now in the opposite direction—and wavelets then expand out to the left of each slit. The wavelets then interfere with each other at the particle source. All of this is exactly as described for the forward wave but in the opposite direction.

Observe: For any particular point P, the path difference along the two particle paths is, of course, the same whether waves travel to the right or to the left along the two paths. Whatever interference would result at point P with the alleged forward wave, exactly the same interference occurs at the particle source with the reciprocal wave. Making allowance for any difference in intensity of the reciprocal and alleged forward waves upon their respective emissions, the intensity of the reciprocal wave from P when it arrives at the particle source will always be equal to the intensity of the alleged forward wave from the particle source when it arrives at P.

Furthermore, as indicated in Section 3.1, a source emits particles only in response to the stimulation provided by a wave. The probability of the emission is proportional to the intensity of the wave at the particle source. But that intensity is, again, equal to the intensity of the quantum mechanical, alleged forward wave at point P. Therefore, the probability of a particle being emitted by the source in response to the wave from point P is equal to the probability determined by quantum mechanics that a particle will be observed at point P.

Once emitted in response to the wave coming from point P, a particle will always travel to point P. The particle has nowhere else to go. In quantum mechanics, a particle must somehow be guided to one of many points on the screen so as to reproduce a pattern determined by the wave, a process shown in Chapter 2 to be inexplicable. In the reciprocal wave picture, after penetrating a slit the particle simply "homes in" on the one point on the screen from which its wave is propagating. No nonlocal interaction with the wave is required to account for this "homing" process. The particle merely responds to the wave at the particle's location and moves in the direction from which the wave is coming. No "quantum weirdness" is required to account for the particle's motion.

Because a particle, once emitted in response to the reciprocal wave from point P, always travels to point P, the overall probability that a particle arrives at P is equal to the probability of the particle's emission, given by the intensity of the reciprocal wave at the particle source. Because that probability is equal to the quantum mechanical probability that the particle arrives at P, the reciprocal wave theory and quantum mechanics make the same prediction of that probability. This is true for every point on the screen. The reciprocal wave theory thus predicts a pattern identical to that predicted by quantum mechanics, which is the pattern observed in the laboratory.

The probability of the entire process by which a particle arrives at any point P is thus determined at the particle source. This probability is not dependent upon a particle's "choice," once it has been emitted, to take one path rather than another while following the wave to point P. In particular, it makes no difference through which slit the particle travels. In order to account for what is observed it is necessary only that the wave direct the particle to point P by one path or the other. The reciprocal wave goes through both slits, but the particle goes through only one of them.

In the theory unfolding here, waves are emanating independently from every point on the screen. Hypothesizing this enormous proliferation of waves might appear to be unreasonable. After all, quantum mechanics "predicts" the same pattern on the screen with only one wave. Yet, in addition to the fact that the experimental evidence refutes the forward-wave picture, quantum mechanics contains the very same proliferation of waves, as indicated in Section 2.4. Quantum mechanics views them as "available states" and not as real waves, the absurdity of which has already been discussed; but they nevertheless form an essential part of quantum mechanical theory.

What we think of as empty space is, in fact, filled with these waves—"elementary waves." The universe does not consist merely of particles in otherwise empty space but instead consists both of particles and waves, the two being entirely separate physical objects in their own right. To the extent of our present knowledge of the universe, both the particles and the waves are "elements" of the universe. Hence the name "elementary waves."

The intensity at the particle source of the reciprocal wave from a particular point P will equal the intensity of the quantum mechanical wave at point P only if the reciprocal wave from P acts independently from the reciprocal waves emanating from all other screen points. Such autonomy requires that the waves emanating from each point on the screen carry a "marker" of some sort set by the state of the atomic or subatomic objects located at that screen point. Exactly what these markers look like is at present unknown. Waves carrying different markers do not interfere with one another. Wavelets from the two slits that carry the same marker interfere with each other and act together as a single wave at the particle source.

When the particle source responds to a particular wave, the wave interference between the two wavelets making up that wave has already taken place. The source then responds to the resulting intensity. According to quantum mechanics, the wave interference relevant to a particle's arrival at a particular point P occurs while the particle is traveling to P. This is one way to see why TEW can explain what occurs but quantum mechanics cannot.

3.3 Quantum Mechanics Refuted

TEW clearly explains the double-slit experiment. Nothing about the picture just presented involves any contradictions—any "weirdness." The theory clearly explains, at least in principle, the process by which individual particles reach the screen, a process that involves no nonlocality. The overall theory clearly explains the pattern observed on the screen.

As explained in Section 2.2, the very fact that this explanation of the double-slit experiment can be put on paper at all, even if it is merely hypothetical—even if it is totally false—refutes quantum mechanics. Quantum mechanics is founded on the claim that no local, non-contradictory theory of any kind could possibly, even in principle, explain the double-slit. Yet here is just such a theory. Whether or not the theory of elementary waves is the correct theory of subatomic phenomena, one conclusion has been proved definitively: quantum mechanics is not the correct theory.

Just to be clear, Chapter 2 already presented the proof that quantum mechanics is false. The findings of each experiment described there blatantly contradict quantum mechanics. The counterexample presented here merely refutes the claim that one has no choice but to accept the contradictions—as if this result should surprise anyone.

As indicated earlier, many modern physicists try to evade the contradictions in quantum mechanics by claiming that it is merely a "formalism" that "works," that they are making no claim that it states what exists in reality, and that this formalism is merely a means of predicting measurements, or "dial readings" on measuring devices. This would amount to treating quantum mechanics as an "as if" theory—the dial readings occur "as if" a wave were coming from the particle source, and "as if" the particle went through both slits, and "as if" time went backward, etc. According to this notion, the "weirdnesses" don't actually exist but dial readings occur "as if" they did. Treated consistently as an "as if" formalism, used while awaiting an actual explanation, quantum mechanics might have some legitimacy. It serves as a mathematical statement of the observed relationships between the dial readings. But clearly this limited utility is not what these physicists have in mind. If it were, then, again, they would have refrained from their continual assertions that modern science has demonstrated that particles can be two places at once, that time can go backward, etc. Clearly they have been thinking about reality all along, and have been drawing conclusions about reality from their formalism. In practice, the claim that quantum mechanics is merely a formalism that works is just one more rationalization for embracing the contradictions—one more instance of the somersault methodology.

For that matter, if physicists really do believe that theories are merely formalisms that "work," on what possible basis could they criticize TEW? It "works." Unlike quantum mechanics, TEW also works, without the quotation marks.

In fairness to the physicists who contributed to the early development of quantum mechanics, we must remember that at the time the forward-wave hypothesis was first accepted, no one had as yet recognized the impossibility of explaining the behaviors of the individual particles under this assumption. By the time it was recognized, so much had already (apparently) been accounted for by the forward-wave theory that no one thought to question it. The forward wave had come to be accepted as an established fact. When contradictions began to appear, physicists thought of them as perhaps reflecting metaphysical differences between the subatomic and macroscopic worlds, differences that were not as yet understood.

But by the time experiments appeared allegedly demonstrating backward-in-time causation and other such preposterous notions, not to speak of proofs that the contradictions could not be eliminated, physicists in general should have recognized that something was seriously wrong with quantum mechanics. Einstein did, but he had very little company. Incredibly, many physicists, including numerous prominent theoreticians in academia, actively opposed and even denounced anyone, including even Einstein—although generally not publicly—who challenged quantum mechanics.

3.4 TEW More Generally

Consider the completely general "scattering" experiment illustrated in Figure 3.4. Particles are emitted by the source at A, they "scatter" off a target of some kind, and some number of the particles arrive at the detector at B. Physicists perform experiments of this kind in order to determine the behavior of particles upon interacting with one another or with larger objects.

Quantum mechanics allegedly accounts for what is observed in any such scattering experiment in the same manner as it does with the double-slit: A wave is emitted from the particle source, it scatters off the target as a wave, and some intensity of wave arrives at the detector. The

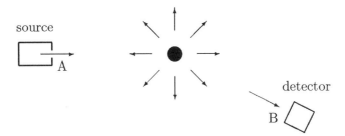

Figure 3.4: General scattering experiment

intensity at the detector yields the probability that a particle will arrive there, this by some unspecified, unreal means.

TEW holds that the wave involved emanates from the detector. The wave scatters off the target, and some intensity of wave arrives at the particle source. The wave at the source stimulates the emission of particles, with a probability proportional to the wave's intensity. The particles then follow the wave, by one path or another—the outcome is the same regardless of the path—to the detector. The particle follows the wave by the local, "homing" process described Section 3.2. Once emitted in response to the wave, the particle follows the wave to the detector with probability 1. The probability of the overall process is thus determined at the particle source by the intensity of the wave that arrives there.

There is a theorem in wave mechanics known as the "reciprocity theorem," one statement of which says that the intensity at point B of a wave emitted at point A will always exactly equal the intensity at point A of an identical wave emitted at point B, this for any kind of wave and any objects with which the waves interact between points A and B.[1] The equality of the interference in both directions in the double-slit

---

[1] Physicists use the term "reciprocal" wave to describe the wave relevant to the "reciprocity" theorem. The wave from B is the "reciprocal" of the wave from A. A reciprocal wave must not be confused with what physicists term a "time-reversed" wave. The "time-reverse" of the wave from point A is obtained by simply reversing the direction of motion of every portion of the wave from A. In the double slit, for example, the alleged quantum mechanical wave from the particle source penetrates the slits and then diverges in all directions. The time-reverse of this would look like a wave converging on the slits from all directions, having emanated from every point on the screen. Clearly the time-reversed wave would look nothing like a reciprocal wave emanating from a single point on the screen.

experiment is not a fluke of that particular experiment but instead is an instance of this completely general theorem.

The remainder of the analysis for the general scattering experiment is then identical to that for the double-slit, demonstrating that TEW always predicts the same probabilities as are "predicted" by quantum mechanics.

The reciprocity principle explains why quantum mechanics has been able to make correct predictions in spite of having the waves moving in the wrong direction. By using the forward wave and computing the intensity at a detector, quantum mechanics yields the numerically correct answer. In order for this to "work," however, it then becomes necessary to somehow transmit everything that actually occurs at the particle source over to the detector. The product is the "weirdness."

A scattering experiment will frequently employ more than one detector. By analogy with the separate points on the screen in the double-slit experiment, each separate point on each separate detector emits waves. As mentioned earlier, the waves carry a "marker" characteristic of their point of origin, and waves carrying different markers do not interfere with one another. The overall physical process by which a particle travels to a particular detection point, whether in the general experiment of Figure 3.4 or in the double-slit, is thus completely independent of the process by which a particle might travel to any other detection point. The waves from different detection points do "compete" with one another at the source in stimulating the emission of particles, but that is their only physical interconnection.

Quantum mechanics, to the contrary, alleges that a single wave from the source is responsible for the probability that a particle arrives at any and all possible detection points. It is impossible to "split" the wave into pieces corresponding to the different points. Modern physicists have proved conclusively that any such split-up would necessarily produce results that differ from what is observed in the laboratory. From this they conclude that the particle, prior to being observed, is not in any state in particular; it is in all states and not in any one of them, "collapsing" into an actual state only upon arrival at a detector. Based on this and other similar arguments, many modern physicists conclude that nothing about the state of the particle or its wave could possibly be the cause of the particle's arrival at one point rather than another. If, prior to the particle's detection, everything is the same regardless of where the particle ends up, how could anything—anything real—possibly account for the behaviors of subatomic particles? Hence the claim to have "refuted reality."

One wonders why these physicists see fit to perform experiments.

3.5 Where the Waves "Come From"

Elementary waves are present at all times throughout all space in the universe. A detector or other object from which elementary waves emanate does not actually create or emit those waves. Instead, the subatomic particles that make up a detector act to rearrange, or "organize," the waves that impinge upon them. No net "quantity of wave" is either created or destroyed in the process.

Waves interact with subatomic particles as they pass by in the immediate neighborhood of the particles. Some waves interact directly with a particle. Other waves interact with waves that have already interacted with the particle.

Waves' interactions with a particle serve to "scatter" the waves in all directions coming out from the particle. Many of the scattered waves will carry a common phase and a common "marker." The common phase and marker constitute the "organization" of these waves. We will speak of waves as "originating" at a detector, but it is only the organization, not the waves themselves, that a detector originates.

3.6 Particle Detectors

When two particles collide and scatter, the interaction can be either "elastic" or "inelastic." In an elastic scattering, the two particles, in effect, bounce off one another and then move apart in new directions. In an inelastic scattering, additional particles are produced. When an electron scatters inelastically off another charged particle, for example, the interaction can produce a photon that also moves apart from the point of interaction, carrying away some of the electron's initial energy. The scattering is termed "inelastic" because the electron loses energy in the process.

It is through inelastic scattering processes that a detector detects a particle that impinges upon it. If the collision of a particle with the particles making up the detector produces a photon, that photon can then be detected by a second detector. Some detectors generate a tiny electrical signal when a particle strikes them and scatters inelastically. That signal can then be amplified and observed.

According to TEW, all particle behavior is governed by the behavior of the elementary waves that the particles follow. While a more complete description of the "following" process must wait until later chapters, one critical fact can be described at this point: It is the inelastic wave interactions—those that will cause a particle following a wave to scatter inelastically—that generate the organized waves leaving a detector. When waves interact inelastically with a particle making up the detector, the particle "implants" the organization on the scattered waves. In an elastic wave scattering, the waves retain the phase and marker implanted on them through a previous inelastic scattering with some other particle.

The process by which a detector organizes waves is the very same process by which the detector detects a particle when it arrives at the detector after following one of those organized waves. Inelastic wave scattering at the detector originates the wave, and that same inelastic wave scattering causes a particle to scatter inelastically—and therefore to be detected—when it arrives at the detector. Clearly this fact is central to the explanation of the double-slit experiment, as it is to TEW in general. Its importance will become further apparent in Chapter 4 when discussing the so-called quantum mechanical "measurement theory."

SCHRÖDINGER'S CAT

4.1 Measurement Theory

Perhaps the single most absurd claim of quantum mechanics is that subatomic particles exist in no state in particular until and unless they are observed, and that it is an observer's act of looking that puts a particle into the state in which it is observed. This claim forms part of a complicated, preposterous, and utterly useless "measurement theory" that has arisen as an essential part of quantum mechanics.

In the pre-quantum, classical era of physics, it was held that objects exist and are what they are independent of their being observed, and that what an object is determines what we see when we look. Observation was thus simply a process of looking and seeing what is there. Quantum mechanics allegedly forces us to abandon this objective view of reality, embracing instead the view that the act of looking determines what exists.

Quantum mechanical measurement theory's claim that looking determines what exists does not merely reiterate the obvious fact that physically distinct measuring devices will present information about an observed object in different forms but with the information in both forms nonetheless reflecting the same specific state of the object. Nor does measurement theory make the equally innocuous claim that the measurement process itself affects or "jostles" the object observed but with the object nonetheless existing in one specific state prior to the "jostling" and a different specific state afterwards. Quantum mechanics asserts that a particle exists not in a single state but in a "superposition of states" until observed, and that the act of observing puts the particle into one of the states making up the "superposition."

The absurdity is carried even further. A measuring device is itself a real object, which, according to this same measurement theory, exists in no state in particular unless observed, and the physical process by which a measuring device interacts with the object measured thus necessarily occurs in many different ways simultaneously until the observation takes place. One therefore cannot say that a measurement has taken place merely because a particle has interacted with a measuring device. Quantum mechanics claims that it is the act by which an observer becomes consciously aware of the result of a measurement that determines the state of the object measured as well as the state of the measuring device. A new theory of measurement is thus allegedly required, a theory in which consciousness is literally incorporated into the very nature of everything we observe.

While there is much controversy among modern physicists regarding the form that this new "measurement theory" should take, it is nonetheless hailed as one of the seminal discoveries of 20th century physics. In fact, it is utterly preposterous. An object cannot exist in no state in particular. To exist is to be something in particular. The only alternative is to be nothing in particular, i.e. nothing—not to exist. If a particle were not anything in particular, to what is it that the words "the particle" might refer?

The view that consciousness determines reality is not a new, progressive innovation but in fact represents a regression in human thought back to the dark ages.

The double-slit experiment illustrates how quantum mechanics forces modern physicists into these absurd conclusions. As described in Section 3.4, according to quantum mechanics, after passing through the two slits, the "wave-particle" must be viewed as propagating from the slits in all directions simultaneously—toward all points on the screen. The wave propagates as a single unit. Blocking a portion of the wave at any point between the slits and the screen changes the pattern over the entire screen. The probability that a particle arrives at any particular point on the screen thus depends on the wave over its entire extent, and not just on a portion travelling toward that one screen point. The "particle" must thus be in all states simultaneously—traveling toward all points on the screen simultaneously—and the act of consciously seeing the particle at a particular point is what puts the particle at that location.

Again, it is not enough, according to quantum mechanics, to conclude that a particle is "observed" merely by its interaction with the screen, thereby producing a "spot" or emitting a photon that might then be observed. The particles in the atoms making up the screen are also allegedly not in any one state, so the interaction with the incident particle must occur in many different ways simultaneously, and if a photon is emitted, that photon also must exist in multiple states. It is the mental act by which an observer becomes conscious of the spot or conscious of the photon that allegedly causes the particle to be located at the spot or at the point from which the photon emanated. Consciousness allegedly determines reality.

But in fact, to be conscious is to be conscious of *something*—something *real*. The only alternative is to be conscious of nothing, i.e., to be unconscious. Objects of which one might become conscious must exist and be what they are before one can become conscious of them. Quantum mechanics does not prove that consciousness determines reality. On the contrary, the fact that the theory leads to this false and preposterous conclusion constitutes still one further refutation of quantum mechanics.

4.2 Polarization of Light

The double-slit experiment involves an enormous number of possible outcomes. Each and every point on the screen where a particle might appear represents a possible outcome. Physicists have performed experiments involving the polarization of light that illustrate the issues discussed in Section 4.1 more simply and directly. In the polarization experiments the number of possible outcomes is reduced to two.[1]

Polarization refers to the orientation of the plane in which a light wave oscillates. In Figure 4.1, the wave on the left illustrates a "vertically"

---

[1] The following analysis allegedly demonstrating the need for a special "measurement theory" employs some of the illustrative methods used in the similar analysis by Professor Robert H. Dicke and Dr. James P. Wittke, *Introduction to Quantum Mechanics*, Addison-Wesley (1960) p. 116ff.

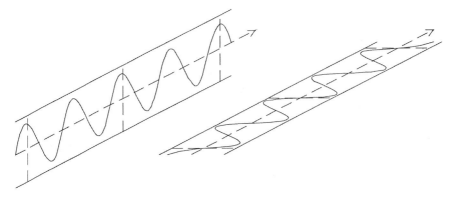

Figure 4.1: Plane polarized waves

polarized wave, the wave on the right a "horizontally" polarized wave. (The terms "vertical" and "horizontal" are relative, merely indicating planes perpendicular to each other.)

Light polarized as shown in Figure 4.1 is termed "plane-polarized" light, so named because the oscillations occur entirely within a single plane. Light can also be "circularly polarized", as illustrated in Figure 4.2. One can think of circular polarization as being a combination of both vertical and horizontal polarization. The oscillations occur in both the vertical and horizontal planes simultaneously, but with the latter shifted by ¼ of a full oscillation relative to the former. In Figure 4.2, the imaginary vertical and horizontal waves that are being combined are shown as dashed curves. The circularly polarized wave is the solid line.

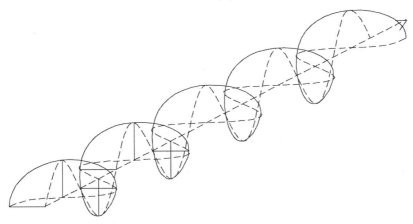

Figure 4.2: Right-handed circularly polarized wave

The long dashed line is the imaginary center line about which the wave circles. The short straight bars—also imaginary—in the first segment of the wave connect the center line with the maxima and minima of the two imaginary plane-polarized waves and thus with the circularly polarized wave itself. They are drawn in as an assistance to visualizing what is actually a three-dimensional picture. As it travels, the wave circles around the center line, hence the term "circular polarization."

By convention, the circularly polarized wave in Figure 4.3 is referred to as being "right-handed." Imagine grabbing the wave with your right hand, and with your thumb pointing in the direction in which the wave is travelling. Your fingers then curl around the wave in the same direction in which it is circling. Light can also be "left-handed" circularly polarized, as illustrated in Figure 4.3. Here you must imagine grabbing the wave with your left hand.

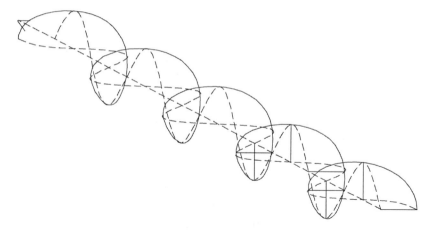

Figure 4.3: Left-handed circularly polarized wave

Just as circular-polarization can be viewed as a combination of vertical and horizontal polarization, so plane-polarization can be viewed as a combination of right- and left-handed circular polarization. Imagine adding together Figures 4.2 and 4.3. The vertical "components" of the two waves are "in phase" with each other, and therefore add to form a wave with twice the amplitude. At the same time, the horizontal components are exactly out of phase with each other and therefore cancel. The two circularly polarized waves add together to form a vertical, plane-polarized wave.

As described in Section 2.4, light consists of both waves and particles, just as with the waves and particles in the double-slit experiment. Indeed, the double slit can be performed using light with (qualitatively) the same results as for other subatomic particles. Quantum mechanics has the light waves moving in the same direction as the photon particles. As before, this forward-wave picture makes it impossible to separate the particle from the wave—to view them as separate entities. Light, according to quantum mechanics, consists of "wave-particles." The wave "part" of these wave-particles can be polarized in any of the ways described above.

An experimenter measures the plane-polarization of a photon by sending it through a device that separates vertical photons from horizontal; vertical photons exit the device through one exit, horizontal another. Similarly for circular polarization, separating photons into right- and left-handed. For ease of illustration in describing the following experiments, a box labelled P (for "Plane") represents a device that divides photons into vertical (V) or horizontal (H) and a box labelled C (for "Circular"), a device that divides photons into right-handed (R) and left-handed (L), as shown in Figure 4.4.

Figure 4.4: Polarization "boxes"

A measurement of a photon's plane polarization will always indicate either vertical or horizontal. One never finds a photon with any polarization in between these two. This is true regardless of the orientation of the polarizer—regardless of the direction arbitrarily chosen as "up," or "vertical." A photon simply leaves the P-box through one exit or the other. The same is true for measurements of circular polarization.

Consider first the experiment illustrated in Figure 4.5. Photons are sent through a P-box, and only the photons that leave the box as vertically polarized are then fed into a second P-box. Photons leaving the first P-box through the horizontal exit are ignored. Detectors are placed behind the two exits of the second P-box to observe through which exit

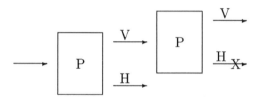

Figure 4.5: First polarization experiment

a photon leaves. It turns out that all photons leaving the second P-box are vertically polarized. A measurement of plane polarization is thus sustained upon measurement by a second P-box.

Next consider the experiment pictured in Figure 4.6. Photons are again fired into a P-box which divides them into vertical or horizontal. Those photons that leave the P-box through the vertical exit are then sent on into a C-box that divides them into right-handed or left-handed. After firing a large number of photons through the two boxes, it turns out that roughly half of the photons register as right-handed and half as left-handed. No prediction of a particular photon's circular polarization can be made following a measurement of its plane polarization.

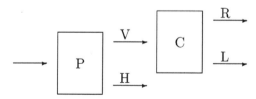

Figure 4.6: Second polarization experiment

Suppose we now add a third box, of the P variety, after the C-box, and allow only the right-handed, circularly polarized photons to enter that box, as illustrated in Figure 4.7. It then turns out that half of the photons exit this third box as vertical and half as horizontal, even though all of them were vertical when they entered the C-box. Quantum mechanics concludes that the measurement of circular polarization—the act of "putting" a photon into one state of circular polarization or the other, or in this case into the right-hand circularly polarized state—destroys any information coming from the measurement of plane polarization in the first P-box—that it is impossible to assign a value to both the plane and the circular polarization at the same time. Measuring one destroys

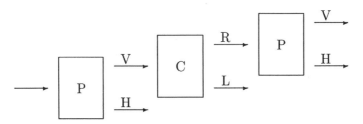

Figure 4.7: Third polarization experiment

the value of the other. Pairs of variables for which the measurement of one destroys the value of the other are termed, in quantum mechanics, "incompatible."

Most peculiar of all—at least to the believers in quantum mechanics—is the result of the experiment illustrated in Figure 4.8. Suppose we insert a fourth box, labeled in the figure as –C, between the C-box and the final P-box of Figure 4.7. This –C-box has the property of reversing whatever was done by the preceding C-box. The –C-box is constructed such that whatever state of polarization a photon has upon entering the combination of C plus –C, it will have the same state upon leaving the combination of boxes. Both the right- and the left-handed photons emerging from the C-box are fed into the –C-box, as shown in the figure. If we now feed the output of the –C-box into a final P-box to measure the final plane polarization, all of the photons emerge from this final P-box as vertically polarized. So, even though the information regarding the vertical polarization observed by the first box is supposedly destroyed by the C-box, that information is "restored" by sending the photons through the –C-box, or so it would appear.

A photon is, supposedly, a localized entity. One would therefore expect that a photon would take one exit or the other from the C-box even if the experimenter didn't know which. Were this the case, one

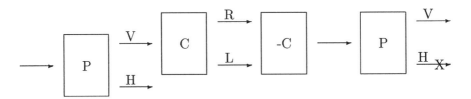

Figure 4.8: Fourth polarization experiment

would further expect that by covering first the R exit and then the L exit, and in each case observing the result following the final P-box, the sum of the two results would equal what is observed with the R and L exits both open. This, in fact, is not what is observed. When either the R or the L exit is covered, half the photons leave the final P-box as vertical, half as horizontal.

These strange results cannot be explained by concluding that when both exits are open, pairs of photons take the two exits from the C-box simultaneously, one photon through each exit, and that the two photons then cooperate with each other while passing through the –C-box. The experiment can be performed in such a manner that the photons pass through the four boxes only one at a time. The result is the same.

Quantum mechanics concludes that when the experimenter doesn't consciously know through which exit a photon left the C-box, the photon doesn't leave through one exit or the other but instead leaves through both exits simultaneously. The measurement by C takes place only if a conscious being actually knows through which exit a photon emerged from C. Without that conscious knowledge, no measurement actually takes place. The photon is neither right-handed nor left-handed upon leaving C; it is in a "superposition" of both states.

Nothing about the state of the photon upon its emission and nothing about the device by which the observation is carried out—in this case by the C-box—has any effect on the outcome. It is only the experimenter's act of becoming consciously aware of the outcome that determines the photon's polarization—or so claims quantum mechanics. Nothing real causes the photon to be either right-handed or left-handed—another alleged "refutation" of reality—only the act of becoming consciously aware of the outcome upon looking.

Some modern physicists have gone so far as to conclude that the very existence of a particle is determined by the act of looking at it. This view produces statements such as that by the Cornell professor, quoted in the Introduction, who claims that science has conclusively determined that the moon doesn't exist when nobody is looking at it. One wonders what the "it" might be at which these physicists look if the moon doesn't exist prior to "it" being looked at. If nothing is there to begin with, mightn't their act of looking be equally likely to produce a ham sandwich?

One of the somewhat less popular versions of "measurement theory" maintains not merely that the state of an object is determined by the observer's act of becoming conscious of it, or even that an act of consciousness creates the particle, but instead that no particles exist at any time; all that exists is consciousness. As stated by Professor Eugene Paul Wigner, Chaired Professor of Mathematical Physics at Princeton University and subsequently a Nobel Laureate, "Physics consists only of relationships between states of consciousness."[2] Professor Wigner also stated explicitly that he did not know what the word "reality" means! One wonders how Professor Wigner or anyone else could become conscious in the first place if nothing existed of which to be conscious.

Modern philosophers, bent as they are on attacking reason and reality, have had a field day with these, and many other, alleged findings of modern physics. They believe that quantum mechanics supports their anti-reality philosophies. However, even if an alleged fact were true—and the above findings of quantum mechanics are not—it is invalid to draw philosophic conclusions from specific facts. The very conclusion that something is a fact presupposes the view that facts are facts, that what one sees is the way things in fact are in reality—in short, presupposes a specific metaphysical philosophy.

4.3 Psycho-Kinetic Felinecide

In 1935, the physicist Erwin Schrödinger proposed a thought experiment—that he certainly had no intention of carrying out—intended to ridicule the notion that the act of becoming conscious of an outcome determines that outcome.[3] The apparatus proposed by Schrödinger differed in some aspects from what I am about to describe but was identical with respect to the point of this thought-experiment.

Imagine starting with the P-box of Figure 4.4. Behind the "horizontal" exit the "experimenter" places a blank screen; if a photon strikes this screen it simply disappears. Behind the "vertical" exit the experimenter places a detector that produces an electrical signal when it detects a photon. The electrical signal operates a device that pulls the trigger on

[2] Private conversation with the author, spring, 1965.
[3] E. Schrödinger, *Naturwissenshaften* **23**, pp. 807-812; 823-828; 844-849 (1935); English translation by J. D. Trimmer, Am. Phil. Soc. **124**, pp.323-338 (1980).

a gun. The gun is aimed at the head of a cat. A device is added that will at some future time emit a single photon in the direction of the P-box. This entire apparatus is then enclosed in a container with walls thick enough to mask any sound of the gun were it to go off, or any other evidence as to what had happened in the box.

As long as no one opens the box and consciously observes through which exit the photon emerges from the P-box—by observing whether the cat is alive or dead—quantum mechanics says that the photon must be in a "superposition" of the two states—both vertical and horizontal. But that would require that the photon has been both detected and not detected, that the signal to the gun has been both sent and not sent, that the gun has been both fired and not fired, and that the cat is both dead and alive. The act of opening the container and looking at the condition of the cat would be the first act by which the experimenter could determine which way the photon went. It would thus be that act that would either kill the cat or grant it a stay of execution. There would be no physical means by which the outcome might be predicted. Whether the cat lives or dies is determined exclusively by the experimenter's becoming consciously aware of the cat's state by looking at it.

Again, Schrödinger proposed this thought experiment for purposes of ridicule. Today the "Schrödinger's cat" experiment appears in many quantum mechanics textbooks with nothing more negative stated about it than that it dramatizes one of the "strange" consequences of quantum mechanics. Clearly standards of scientific reasoning have disintegrated sharply since Schrödinger's time.

4.4 TEW Rescues the Cat

TEW explains these polarization experiments without any special measurement theory. The waves involved are traveling in the opposite direction, from the detectors through the boxes and ultimately to the particle source. The "exits" of the boxes now become entrances for these reciprocal, elementary waves. The boxes transmit the same waves in the reverse direction that they are alleged to transmit in the forward direction in the quantum mechanical picture.

In all of the experiments, for any path by which an alleged forward "wave-particle" travels from the source to a detector in the quantum mechanical picture, an elementary wave from that detector travels through the system to the particle source. The source then emits particle photons in response to that wave, and the photons follow the wave to the detector. When no path exists that would transmit a "wave-particle" to a detector according to the quantum mechanical picture, no wave from that detector makes it through the system to the photon source in the elementary wave picture, so no particles will be emitted in response to that wave, and no particles will reach that detector.

In every case the result is exactly as quantum mechanics predicts. Yet in the reciprocal wave picture, no particle ever need be in two states simultaneously, nor does the consciousness of an observer in any way affect the outcome. In the experiment of Figure 4.8, where quantum mechanics "requires" that a wave-particle be in two states simultaneously, in TEW there are simply two waves. The particle photon then follows one wave or the other as it travels back to the wave's source. As in the double slit, the outcome is the same regardless of the photon's path. The presence or absence of the wave at the photon source has already determined whether or not a photon reaches the detector in question. The boxes affect the waves in the same manner whether or not anyone observes the result, and the particle photons simply follow their wave to the detector. It is really that simple.

Quantum mechanics cannot arrive at this simple solution because, as revealed by the double slit experiment, it is impossible to separate the wave from the particle. With TEW, the wave is an independent entity existing prior to the particle's emission.

Consider specifically the elementary waves from the upper detector behind the second P-box in the third experiment, Figure 4.7. Figure 4.9 illustrates the TEW explanation of that experiment. The detector emits waves of all polarizations. Only the vertical plane-polarized waves pass

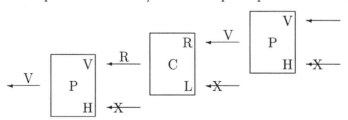

Figure 4.9: TEW explanation of third experiment

through the P-box when entering through the vertical "exit." A plane-polarized wave consists, in effect, of two circularly polarized waves, as explained in Section 4.2. The right-handed circularly polarized "half" is transmitted through the C-box from the right-handed "exit." That wave then impinges on the vertical "exit" of the first P-box. The circularly polarized wave consists of two plane-polarized waves, and the vertical "half" is transmitted through the P-box to the particle source. So particles are stimulated from the source, and they follow that wave to the detector. A similar analysis shows that waves from a detector placed behind the H exit of the second P box also reach the particle source. So particles reach both detectors

The only complication is in the fourth experiment, the TEW explanation of which is illustrated in Figure 4.10. The –C-box now acts as a C-box did on the alleged forward wave, and the C-box acts as a –C. The C-box (now acting as a –C) will undo what was done to the wave by the –C-box only if both waves that come out of the –C-box go into the C-box. The two waves, because they came from a common source—the wave entering the –C-box—are what physicists describe as being "coherent" with one another, meaning that the two can be put back together to reconstitute what entered the –C-box to begin with. (This is exactly what allegedly occurs when the forward waves recombine in the quantum mechanical picture.) When both waves are fed into the C-box from the –C-box, vertical waves from the second P-box recombine to vertical waves, and horizontal waves from the second P-box recombine into horizontal waves. The latter cannot make it through the vertical exit of the first P-box, so they don't reach the particle source. No particles then travel through to the detector behind the horizontal exit of the second P-box, as in the quantum mechanical picture. If only one wave or the other is fed into the C-box, each has both horizontal and vertical components, so both of the latter are fed into the vertical "exit" of the

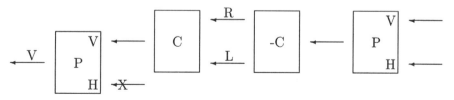

Figure 4.10: TEW explanation of fourth experiment

first P. This is true regardless of the polarization of the plane-polarized wave entering the –C-box from the second P-box. So waves from both detectors behind the second P-box will make it through to the photon source, and photons will then be observed at both detectors.

Again, in every case, the result obtained is exactly what quantum mechanics predicts and exactly what is in fact observed in the laboratory. At no time does the particle photon exist in multiple states—an alleged "superposition of states." The wave splits into two waves and takes both routes through the combination of the C and the –C; the particle takes only one route or the other. The whole notion of some new measurement theory simply evaporates.

Measurement theory is one essential aspect of the subject of the multitude of papers, books, international conferences, etc., mentioned in Section 2.2 in the context of the double-slit experiment. And, as shown again here, all of this mountain of writing and analysis is the utterly useless and meaningless consequence of a mistake—the mistake of assuming that the wave moves in the forward direction.

Consciousness does not create reality. Objects must exist and be what they are before we can become conscious of them.

Chapter 5

HEISENBERG'S UNCERTAINTY PRINCIPLE

5.1 The Alleged Principle

The Heisenberg "uncertainty principle" has received perhaps more publicity than any other aspect of modern subatomic physics. The "principle" is also complete nonsense.

The principle, in its most conspicuous application, states that the position of a particle and its velocity cannot both have exact values at any one time. The principle does not merely say that we cannot accurately observe both the position and the velocity of a particle due to the limits of our means of observation, but instead maintains that *in actuality* a particle's position and/or velocity is/are "uncertain"—that one parameter or the other or both has/have no value in particular.

In fact, no real parameter of any real object can have no value in particular. To exist is to be *something*—something in particular. The only alternative is to be nothing in particular, i.e., nothing—not to exist. Apparently modern physicists think "nothing in particular" is a new kind of something, or at least this is true of those physicists who believe that anything exists at all. By any rational standard, the fact that quantum mechanics leads to "uncertainty" in the state of real objects constitutes still one more iron-clad refutation of quantum mechanics.

The principle is generally stated not in terms specifically of the velocity of a particle but instead in terms of a particle's momentum. The momentum p of a particle is equal to its mass m times its velocity v:

$$p=mv.$$

Mathematically the principle states:

$$\Delta x \times \Delta p \geq h,$$

where Δx stands for the uncertainty in the position x and Δp stands for the uncertainty in the momentum p. Their product is always greater than or equal to Planck's constant h, a tiny constant characteristic of the scale of subatomic phenomena. The more precise the position of a particle, and therefore the smaller the "uncertainty" in its position, the more uncertain is the momentum, and vice versa, with the product of the two uncertainties being at least as large as Planck's constant.

The Kaiser experiment described in Section 2.3 presents a real-world illustration of the principle. As discussed in that section, the interferometer will transmit waves whose frequencies lie within only a narrow range, or "band-width," of frequencies. Although the individual waves at each frequency have an amplitude throughout the apparatus, quantum mechanics maintains that the waves do not act independently from one another but instead add together in such a way that their sum is zero throughout most of the apparatus and is non-zero over only a short length somewhere in the apparatus. The resulting "object," or "wave-packet" as it was referred to in Section 2.3—the length over which the net amplitude is non-zero—moves through the apparatus and in some unstated manner represents the particle. Mathematically,[1] the shorter the wave packet, and therefore the more precise the position of the particle, the wider the range of frequencies required to add up to that wave packet. By the same token, the narrower the range of frequencies, the longer the minimum wave-packet length to which the waves can add up. For purposes of this qualitative discussion, a range of frequencies corresponds to a range of momenta. So everywhere in this paragraph, the term "frequency" can be replaced with the term "momentum" and the description remains the same.

According to quantum mechanics, because the waves at all frequencies add together and act together in determining how a particle behaves, the particle can never follow just one of the waves and thereby have the one specific momentum determined by that one single wave. Quantum mechanics requires that the uncertainty in momentum exist

---

[1] Through a branch of mathematics known as "Fourier analysis", with which the reader needn't be familiar.

within, as if being a property of, the neutron wave-particle. The same is true for the position of the particle, i.e., where within the length of the wave-packet "the neutron" is located.

This, then, is how quantum mechanics accounts for the Heisenberg relationship.

5.2 TEW Explanation

TEW explains the Kaiser experiment, thereby doing away with the uncertainty principle, in a manner that is simple in concept but nonetheless somewhat involved. According to TEW, the waves are, as always, moving in the opposite direction: from each detector through the apparatus and to the particle source. Referring back to Figure 2.6, each wave from each detector splits and takes both paths through the interferometer. Interference between the waves taking the two paths takes place at what was the first crystal in the quantum mechanical description. Under some conditions the interference will send the wave up toward the neutron particle source; under other conditions it will send it down and out of the picture. A detector will detect a particle only if a wave from that detector scattered up toward the neutron source where it stimulated the emission of the particle, which particle then follows the wave to the detector.

As described above, the apparatus will accommodate a small bandwidth of frequencies. But in TEW each wave at each frequency acts entirely independently from the other waves. TEW involves no magical combination into wave packets. When a wave of a particular frequency arrives at the neutron source, the source can emit a particle in response to the stimulation of that wave. A particle so emitted then follows that one wave to the detector from which the wave originated. Each particle is emitted in response to one wave or another in the bandwidth, not to some combination of the waves.

When a wave splits at crystal #3 and then recombines at crystal #1, what makes the combination scatter either up or down is, as before, the relative phase of the two waves when they rejoin. If the two are exactly in phase, the combination will scatter one way (up or down), and if exactly out of phase, the other. If the two are somewhat out of phase, the wave will scatter partly up toward the particle source and partly downward, away from the particle source.

At crystal #3, the elementary waves from one detector divide in a manner such that the two "halves" start their journey through the interferometer exactly in phase. The waves from the other detector will divide and start their journey exactly out of phase. This is the inverse of what occurs at the first crystal when the waves recombine. In the absence of any bismuth, if the interferometer is perfectly aligned, then whatever the relative phase of the two waves is when they divide, the relative phase will be the same when they recombine. The waves from one detector will thus scatter one way, the waves from the other detector the other way. Particles will then arrive at only one of the two detectors.

Assume for the purposes of this explanation that, in the absence of any bismuth to slow down the waves in the upper path, the alignment of the apparatus is such that all waves from the lower detector are exactly in phase at the first crystal and deflect up toward the neutron source, and all waves from the upper detector are exactly out of phase and deflect down, away from the source.

Consider, then, a single wave at a single frequency coming from the lower detector. With no bismuth in place, the waves on the two paths are exactly in phase when they arrive at crystal #1 and scatter up. Suppose, then, that a small amount of bismuth, enough to slow the wave down by ½ wavelength, is placed in the upper path. Under these circumstances, the waves on the two paths will be exactly out of phase when they meet at crystal #1, and the combination will scatter down. In the absence of any bismuth, the wave from the upper detector is exactly out of phase at crystal #1 and scatters down. Adding, again, just enough bismuth to slow down the wave in the upper path by ½ wavelength, the waves from the upper detector will then be in phase at crystal #1 and will scatter up.

This same description applies to the waves at all frequencies in the bandwidth allowed by the interferometer. Because all waves in the allowed bandwidth have very close to the same wavelength, the small amount of bismuth just added will cause all the waves to shift by approximately the same ½ wavelength. As a result, the waves at all allowed frequencies coming from each individual detector will act in an identical manner.

But what happens when enough bismuth is added to slow all the waves down by many wavelengths? The slight difference in wavelength between the various waves will then start to make a difference to the outcome. A wave of a longer wavelength might be slowed down by, say, 2000 of its own wavelengths, while a wave of a shorter wavelength might simultaneously be slowed down by 2000.5 of its wavelengths. In this case, the bismuth will produce opposite effects for the two waves even though both came from the same detector. The wave slowed down by an even 2000 wavelengths will rejoin its other half with the same relative phase as was the case with no bismuth and will scatter exactly as it had with no bismuth. But the wave that shifted by the 2000.5 wavelengths will now have exactly the opposite relative phase at the first crystal, so those waves will scatter in the opposite direction.

As an aid to picturing this situation, Figure 5.1 shows two waves, in phase at the beginning on the left but out of phase by ½ wavelength on the right. If each wave slows by an amount equal to the total length shown in the figure, then even though the length of the slowdown is the same for both, their relative phase will nonetheless change.

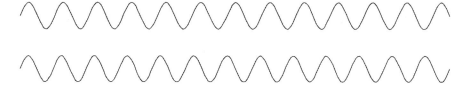

Figure 5.1: Shift from in-phase to out-of-phase

If enough bismuth is added so that every wave shifted by a particular fraction of a wavelength can be paired with a wave at another frequency—still coming from the same detector—shifted by that same fraction plus ½ wavelength, waves from each detector will scatter equally in both directions. Therefore, regardless of the addition of further bismuth, waves from both detectors will arrive with equal intensity at the particle source, and particles will thus arrive equally at both detectors. The interference will appear to be gone.

Observe, however, that each individual wave at each individual frequency still self-interferes at the first crystal, exactly as if all the other waves at other frequencies weren't present. So in fact all of the interference remains. But because the waves at different frequencies interfere differently, some particles go up and some down, and it appears as if the interference has stopped.

5.3 Mathematical Derivation with No Uncertainties

Putting this mathematically, suppose the wave of longest wavelength in the band-width has a wavelength λ that is longer than that of the wave of shortest wavelength by an amount $\Delta\lambda$. When the bismuth reaches the thickness that slows the waves enough that the wave of shortest wavelength is shifted by one full wavelength more than the wave of longest wavelength, every wave at every wavelength in between will have a "partner" that is shifted by ½ wavelength relative to itself, so all of the "interference" will appear to stop. The number n of wavelengths by which the waves must be slowed in order to meet this condition is thus the number such that

$$n \times \Delta\lambda = \lambda,$$

or

$$n = \frac{\lambda}{\Delta\lambda}.$$

The length of the slowdown is, according to quantum mechanics, the "uncertainty" Δx in the position of a particle, so that "uncertainty" is given by

$$\Delta x = n \times \lambda = \frac{\lambda^2}{\Delta\lambda}.$$

The momentum of a particle is related to the wavelength of the wave it follows, according to quantum mechanics as well as TEW, by the formula

$$p = \frac{h}{\lambda},$$

where h again is Planck's constant. Some elementary calculus then says that a small change Δp in the momentum is related to a small change $\Delta\lambda$ in the wavelength by

$$\Delta p = -\frac{h}{\lambda^2} \times \Delta\lambda.$$

The minus sign has no significance; whether a number is too large by a certain amount or too small by the same amount, the "uncertainty" is the same either way. Finally, then,

$$\Delta p \times \Delta x = \frac{h}{\lambda^2} \times \Delta\lambda \times \frac{\lambda^2}{\Delta\lambda} = h,$$

which is exactly the Heisenberg relationship. TEW hereby explains Heisenberg's formula.

Nowhere in this picture does any object exist in anything other than an exact state. Each wave is a wave of an exact frequency. Many frequencies come into play because there are many waves, but the waves do not "coalesce." Each particle is emitted in response to only one wave and hence has exactly the one momentum corresponding to that wave at all times. A particle is always located at one point at all times.

5.4 A is A

In subatomic phenomena in general, what gives rise to the appearance of "uncertainties" is the presence of more than a single wave. The waves of different frequency will act differently—in some circumstances quite differently. Once a particle is emitted in response to one of the waves, its behavior is strictly determined. Nevertheless, because one cannot determine in advance to which of the several waves a particular particle will respond upon its emission, one cannot predict a particular particle's behavior with certainty.

The inability of the experimenter to predict to which of the waves the source will respond does not imply any "uncertainty" in the source. By the time the source emits a particle in response to one wave or another, all of the wave interference relevant to the outcome has already taken place. Straightforward mathematical arguments then show that the inability of the experimenter to predict the behavior of the source can be explained as resulting simply from the experimenter's lack of knowledge of the value of some parameter or parameters in the source, and not to any intrinsic "uncertainty" inherent in the actual values of those parameters. In quantum mechanics, the motion of a particle occurs while the relevant wave interference is still taking place. As a result, quantum mechanics is forced to incorporate the unpredictability into the very dynamics of the particle. Hence the uncertainty principle.

Quantum mechanics gets into trouble because in that theory the state of a particle is determined at the detector. But the unpredictability is in fact the product of what happens at the particle source. In order for quantum mechanics to account for what is observed, somehow the unpredictability has to be conveyed from the source to the detector. Hence the conclusion that the particle's state while it travels is uncertain, that it travels in no state in particular but in all states simultaneously, etc. The physical situation surrounding the alleged uncertainty principle puts in bold relief how it is that the forward-wave hypothesis leads to the many weirdnesses of quantum mechanics.

The fact that the behavior of a particular particle cannot be predicted with certainty is a fact. As such it warrants explanation. Why is it that one particle acts differently from another under what appear to be identical circumstances? TEW explains this in clear, simple terms: a different wave produces a different behavior. The quantum mechanical "uncertainty principle" explains absolutely nothing. The import of the "principle" is that the difference in behaviors of different particles is inexplicable—it just happens—for no reason. All that modern physicists have done here is to substitute the two words "uncertainty principle" for the observed unpredictability and to represent this substitution as a bold new scientific discovery.

Modern physicists and philosophers frequently disparage an explanatory approach to science by representing it as being nothing more that an attempt to deduce facts from allegedly self-evident but in fact arbitrary principles. Modern physicists themselves are guilty of this sort of "reasoning," but they have carried the unreason even further. The alleged "self-evident principles" they cite in their criticisms of what they incorrectly describe as explanatory science generally purport to be identifying something that is at least real; the words in those alleged principles at least mean something identifiable, even if they add up to a fantasy. The modern physicist doesn't even get that far. He simply embraces the unexplained phenomenon, invents one or two words adding up to nothing even potentially identifiable, and pretends thereby to have discovered something profound.

Since its inception, the uncertainty principle has served as a major roadblock to progress in the study of subatomic particles. The ultimate purpose of studying subatomic particles is, of course, to discover what they are made up of—what they "look like" inside. But according to quantum mechanics, a particle cannot have inner parts, because if it did, the parts would necessarily violate the uncertainty principle. The inner parts would be confined in their location to a volume no larger than the size of the particle itself. The "uncertainty" in the position of each of the parts would thus have to be no larger than the particle, which would be very small. As a result, the uncertainty in momentum of each part would be enormous; each inner part would necessarily have a momentum far greater than any that could possible allow it to be confined within the particle. Modern physicists have concluded that even the suggestion of an inner structure of particles is meaningless. So they haven't looked for one. Chapter 11, dealing in part with what modern physicists have termed "parity violation"—another pair of words identifying nothing— lists a number of totally obvious and highly valuable conclusions from which physicists have been blocked by this absurd "reasoning."

Observe, once again, the somersaulting. This no-particle-structure argument obviously presumes that the uncertainty principle is not merely part of a formalism that "works" but is instead a causal principle producing real physical consequences—exactly what modern physicists claim to have "risen above" in their "modern," purely descriptive, non-explanatory view of science.

There are no "uncertainties" in reality. All real objects—and there are none other—are what they are. A is A.

Chapter 6

BELL'S THEOREM

6.1 Einstein vs. Bohr

During the years when quantum mechanics was beginning to take form, a protracted debate occurred between Albert Einstein and the physicist Niels Bohr. Although Einstein appeared at times to accept the view that physics is non-explanatory and consists merely of a mathematical description of behavior, he nonetheless anchored his thinking firmly in reality. Physical phenomena, in Einstein's view, occur as they do for a reason, a reason to be found in the makeup of the real objects involved. Nothing happens by chance. The physical parameters of objects necessarily have specific numerical values. Bohr maintained that the findings of quantum mechanics had refuted this reality-based view. The various "weirdnesses" described in earlier chapters of this work proved, according to Bohr, that a universe of real objects having definite properties and acting accordingly was a fantasy. As modern descendants of Bohr's views express matters, principles such as causality, the rules of logic, etc., are useless, "old-fashioned metaphysics" and have no place in physical science. Bohr, however, in spite of his explicitly stated anti-reality views, would, like many modern physicists, frequently base his reasoning on these very principles when it was convenient and simultaneously would freely ignore them when that was convenient. His aim was to discover formulas that "work", by hook or by crook.

In 1935, in an effort to preserve his philosophic view in the face of quantum mechanics, Einstein, along with physicists B. Podolsky and N. Rosen, published an article[1] which argued that quantum mechanics had

---

[1] A. Einstein, B. Podolsky, and N. Rosen, "Can quantum-mechanical description of reality be considered complete?", *Physical Review* **47** (1935) pp. 777-780 .

to be "incomplete." Judging from what is said in the article, it appears that Einstein accepted quantum mechanics as far as it went. The problem, Einstein held, was that something was missing. As he expressed it in the article, a physical theory is complete only if "every element of the physical reality" has "a counterpart in the physical theory." By expressing his view in this manner, Einstein was conforming to the then (and now) popular view that a theory is a self-contained symbolic formalism that is somehow "sandwiched" on reality. It is nonetheless clear from these quotations that he held the view that physics is a science about physical reality and that a theory is a theory only if it expresses what exists in reality. The article also stated, "If, without in any way disturbing a system, we can predict with certainty the value of a physical quantity, then there exists an element of physical reality corresponding to this physical quantity." Again, Einstein was conforming to the "formalism" view, but—expanding somewhat on what he said—he was nonetheless maintaining that our ability to predict any behavior is based on the fact that all behavior is produced by something real. Because the real something is something specific—it is what it is—it will always act accordingly, hence we can predict how it will act in the future. Because there exists no basis upon which behavior might otherwise be predicted, if a particular behavior is predictable, then something real must exist to cause that behavior. This was Einstein's view and was the view held, at least implicitly, by the majority of physicists prior to the 20th century. It was diametrically opposed to the view of Bohr, who militated against the validity of any such principles.

Einstein, Podolsky and Rosen (EPR) based their incompleteness argument on a thought experiment, illustrated in Figure 6.1. Two particles are emitted as a pair from the source in the center. The particles travel out from the source in opposite directions and arrive at devices that measure one or another of their properties.

Because the two particles are created together as a pair, the measured values of some of the properties of one particle will be uniquely related to the measured values of the same properties of the second particle. An actual measurement of one of these properties of one particle thus permits an experimenter to predict with certainty the value that he would obtain by measuring the same property of the second particle.

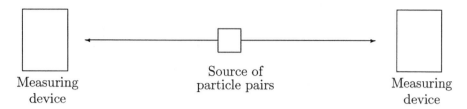

Figure 6.1: EPR experiment

Consider two such properties, chosen so as to be mutually "incompatible." As defined in Section 4.2, measurement of one property of a particle destroys the value of another "incompatible" property of that same particle. Suppose, then, that the experimenter measures first one and then the other of the two incompatible properties of one of the two particles in the EPR experiment. Although the experimenter can measure only one of the two properties of this "first" particle at a specific time, he might measure either one, and either measurement would allow him to predict with certainty the value for the other particle. Furthermore, the state of the second particle is in no way affected by the measurements made on the first particle; at the time the experimenter observes the first particle, the second particle is some distance away. Because the experimenter could predict the value of either property of the second particle with certainty without changing its state, there must be an "element of physical reality" corresponding to each property—something unknown in the makeup of the second particle that would explain the result of each measurement that might be performed. Because the quantum mechanical description of the state of the second particle does not allow both variables to have specific values, something has to be missing from that description. Quantum mechanics must be "incomplete", or so argued Einstein et. al.

EPR thus argued from quantum mechanics itself that the inability of quantum mechanics to predict the values that would be obtained from a measurement of a property of a particle necessarily reflects missing information. Some "hidden variables", as they came to be called, must exist in a particle, knowledge of the numerical values of which would permit an exact prediction of any property—any behavior—of the particle. The unpredictability of a particle's behavior does not mean that the behavior occurs for no reason.

Bohr argued, in effect, that it is impossible in principle to account for the "weirdnesses" of quantum mechanics by means of any appeal to alleged missing information—any appeal to "hidden variables." And, were quantum mechanics a correct theory, and were it still to act as the basis for a more "complete" theory, Bohr would clearly have been correct, as demonstrated in earlier chapters of this work and in what follows. Quantum mechanics, including all its weirdnesses, won the day.

As is usually the case when human beings adhere to an irrational point of view, forward-wave quantum mechanics became a rigid dogma among physicists in the years following the Einstein-Bohr debate. Opposition to any challenge to quantum mechanics became so fierce that any physicist who even mentioned the phrase "hidden variables" risked destroying his reputation or even ending his career. Incredibly, this fanaticism resulted even in the marginalization of Einstein himself.

Although Einstein was basically correct in his philosophical position, he was incorrect in his view of the origin of the "problem" of quantum mechanics. Quantum mechanics cannot be "fixed" by adding anything to it. It is already incorrect as it stands. Once the forward-wave hypothesis had become part of the theory, the damage had already been done. Einstein did err philosophically when he accepted quantum mechanics as being correct even as a partial theory because it "worked"—because it correctly predicted the results of experiments. That philosophic view is clearly false. Quantum mechanics does "work" in that sense but it is totally nonsensical. Einstein attempted for many years to "fix" quantum mechanics but was blocked by this error. He continued to look for additions to quantum mechanics rather than for errors in the theory as already formulated.

Bohr, more than any other figure, was the initiator of the 20th century's philosophical disintegration leading to today's nightmare of unreason known as "modern physics." His view, in essence (if such a term can be applied to anything having to do with Bohr) still prevails today. He is generally considered to have "won" the Bohr-Einstein debate. In fact, as will become clear later in this chapter if it is not clear already, Einstein had the correct philosophic view all along, but, not having discovered the correct physical theory of subatomic particles, was unable to sustain his view under the onslaught of quantum mechanics.

6.2 EPR Experiments

Modern physicists have performed Einstein's thought experiment multiple times in the laboratory since the publication of the EPR paper. In a terrible irony, they claim that the results prove the completeness of quantum mechanics—that nothing is "missing"—and the existence of nonlocality, the exact opposite of what Einstein had intended. Modern physicists claim that the behaviors revealed by EPR experiments cannot possibly be the product of any real properties of the particles involved.

These experiments all follow the pattern of the above Figure 6.1. Most commonly, the particles involved are photons and the measuring devices are polarizers, or P-boxes, as described in Chapter 4 and illustrated in Figure 4.4. A detector is placed behind each "exit" of the polarizer/P-box to observe through which exit a photon left. Each polarizer can be rotated to observe the plane polarization at various angles. As in the thought experiment, the polarizations of the two photons are correlated, resulting from their having been emitted as a pair and not as two separate, individual photons. It is found, for example, that if the two polarizers have been rotated by the same angle, so that the "vertical" on one side is parallel to the "vertical" on the other and the "horizontal" is likewise parallel to the "horizontal," then whenever the photon on one side is observed to be vertically polarized, the photon on the other side will always be observed as horizontally polarized. This result occurs for any angle by which the polarizers have been mutually rotated.[2]

The polarization of each photon is unknown upon its emission. According to quantum mechanics, whatever state of polarization is observed for a photon, the photon is put into that state by the polarizer—that is, by the experimenter's act in becoming conscious of the fact that the photon left the P-box through a particular exit. Quantum mechanics maintains that, prior to the observation, a photon exists in a "superposition of states."

The plane polarization measured with the polarizer at one orientation is "incompatible" with the plane polarization measured with

---

[2] The correlation described here is what results from the specific two-particle source that many experimenters have chosen for their experiments. Different correlations might result from different particle sources.

the polarizer rotated by some angle (with the exception of rotations by multiples of 90 degrees, which might merely reverse the vertical and horizontal). Suppose we were to repeat the "First Polarization Experiment" illustrated in Figure 4.5 but with the second P-box rotated by 45 degrees relative to the first. Even though all photons entering the second P-box are vertically polarized relative to the first box (the horizontally polarized photons are sent elsewhere and ignored), half of the photons would leave the rotated P-box as "vertical" and half as "horizontal," much like what occurred in the second polarization experiment, illustrated in Figure 4.6, using the C-box. Measurement of the plane-polarization at one polarizer orientation allows no prediction of a measurement of plane-polarization by a second polarizer rotated by 45 degrees relative to the first. According to quantum mechanics, a photon cannot possibly have exact values for both plane-polarizations. The two are "incompatible" and thus are suitable for the EPR experiment.

In the majority of the experiments that physicists have performed, the correlations they observe are not as simple as the ones just described. Instead, they measure the polarizations with the polarizers rotated by angles that differ from one another by varying amounts. By observing at each relative orientation how frequently a photon pair is observed to be either vertical on both sides, or vertical on one side and horizontal on the other or both horizontal, experimenters measure the probability that a pair will be emitted with each relative polarization.

According to a famous theorem proved by the physicist J. S. Bell,[3] it is mathematically impossible to account for the correlations actually observed in the experiment by attributing them to properties, "hidden" or otherwise, carried by the individual particles. One can account for the behavior of a particle at its polarizer only if it is also affected by the orientation of the opposite polarizer.

One might then conclude that there must be a physical interaction of some sort between the two polarizers. Perhaps it is interactions such as this that are missing from quantum mechanics, interactions without which quantum mechanics is "incomplete."

---

[3] J.S. Bell, On the Einstein-Podolsky-Rosen paradox, *Physics* **1** (1964) pp 195-200.

An allegedly definitive experiment, generally referred to as the "Innsbruck experiment," has been performed[4] eliminating the possibility of any such communication. The experiment follows the same plan as that illustrated in Figure 6.1, with one modification: Instead of fixing each polarizer at a particular orientation before a photon pair is emitted, each polarizer is rotated into its final position once the two photons are already in flight. Because the photons travel at the speed of light, and because, according to Einstein's well confirmed theory of relativity, no signal can travel faster than the speed of light, any signal that might be emitted by a polarizer following its "delayed" rotation would not have time to reach the opposite polarizer before the photon on that side arrived. There would thus be no possible physical means by which the two polarizers could interact so as to affect the outcome.

The experiment found no change in the correlations. The observed correlations were exactly those predicted by quantum mechanics, and, again, were such as could not be explained (according to the quantum mechanical picture of the experiment) as resulting from the actions of any alleged "hidden variables."

Modern physicists have concluded that nothing real can explain the results of the experiment—that the experiment "refutes reality." The experiment allegedly provides an explicit example of nonlocal behavior; the two sides of the experiment allegedly interact nonlocally, that is, by no means.

First of all, this latter conclusion is totally groundless, even assuming the correctness of quantum mechanics. Given the "method" of quantum mechanics applied elsewhere, as for example in the Kaiser experiment described in Section 2.3, physicists might just as "reasonably" have concluded that the experiment demonstrates backwards-in-time causation. The observation of the polarization of one photon would determine, backwards in time, what had happened when the two photons were emitted, thus giving the opposite photon the "information" needed to choose the correct polarization at its polarizer. The choice between nonlocality and backwards-in-time, aside from the fact that

---

[4] Gregory Weihs, Thomas Jennewein, et. al., "Violation of Bell's Inequality under Strict Einstein Locality Conditions," *Physical Review Letters* **81**, #23, 7 December, 1998, pp. 5039-5043.

both choices are absurd, is totally arbitrary. There is thus no factual basis for concluding that the experiment reveals either one.

As discussed in Section 3.3, if quantum mechanics is treated consistently as merely the formalism-that-works that it is alleged to be, there is no factual basis for concluding that any of the "quantum weird-nesses" are real anyway, even on quantum mechanics' own terms. This fact hasn't stopped modern physicists. Even though they have relegated explanations to the dustbin of scientific history, they have no problem with the claim that it is nonlocality that explains the correlations. After all, this "explanation" makes absolutely no sense, so by accepting it they still haven't committed the sin of attributing the behaviors to anything real.

Indeed, the experiment itself dictates the conclusion that the alleged nonlocal interaction is unreal. The very premise behind the addition of delayed choice to the experiment is that nothing can travel faster than the speed of light. But the alleged nonlocal interaction would be instantaneous, and therefore faster than the speed of light. Were this interaction real—were it carried out by a real physical process—then something could travel faster than the speed of light, in which case the delayed choice would not rule out interaction between the two polar-izers, and therefore the experiment does not confirm nonlocality. But if the interaction is unreal, that means it doesn't exist. How could a non-existent interaction explain anything?

By performing an experiment designed specifically around the as-sumption that nothing can travel faster than the speed of light, physicists actually allege to have proved that something can travel faster than the speed of light!

It was bad enough when the "para-psychologists" at Duke University claimed to have demonstrated the existence of mental te-lepathy. Now modern physicists want us to believe that there can be what amounts to telepathy between photons!

Observe again the somersault philosophy: Physicists assume the law of cause and effect when they argue that something must explain the correlations between the polarizations, but they then conclude that nothing real could explain it—that they have refuted reality.

When all the rationalizing is swept away, the simple truth is that quantum mechanics cannot explain the correlations observed in the

Innsbruck experiment. Nonlocality is a non-starter, as is backwards-in-time causation or any of the other similar fantasies invented to account for other experiments. Still one more time, the evidence seen in the laboratory refutes quantum mechanics.

6.3 Reality is Real

As always, quantum mechanics leads to the above absurd conclusions because it has the waves moving in the wrong direction.[5] Referring again to Figure 6.1, the waves that the photons follow are, in fact, moving inward, from the polarizers to the two-particle source. As demonstrated in Chapter 4, the mistaken assumption that the waves move in the forward direction forces physicists falsely to conclude that, while traveling from the source to their respective polarizers, the photons do not have any polarization in particular but are instead in a superposition of states of various different polarizations. The experimenter's conscious awareness of the results of the polarization measurements then determines—at the polarizers—the actual polarizations.

In fact, the two particle source determines everything. The manner in which each photon will act at its polarizer, for any orientation of the polarizer, is determined upon emission of the photon pair at the particle source, and thus while the two photons are still together at the same location. Whatever interaction between the photons might be involved in making the determinations, that interaction is strictly local.

Each individual photon would, of course, have to carry parameters of some sort that would cause the photon to act one way or the other—vertical or horizontal—at its polarizer. But these parameters would not be the equivalent of the hidden variables whose existence is refuted by Bell's theorem. Quantum mechanics, even assuming nonlocal interactions, does not predict what the polarization of each individual photon will be. Instead it predicts the probability of one outcome or the other. The probabilities vary as one varies the orientation of a polarizer. But the variation in the probabilities occurs in a smooth, continuous manner. Bell's theorem proves that no such smoothly varying probability

---

[5] The author's 1996 paper on TEW (Theory of Elementary Waves, *Physics Essays* **9**, 1), included the erroneous statement that TEW does not explain EPR experiments with delayed choice, but in fact TEW does explain such experiments.

distribution, applied at each polarizer, could possibly account for the observed correlations unless there is interaction between the two sides. In the TEW picture, no such smoothly varying distribution is conveyed to the polarizers. What the photons do convey is a simple yes or no—vertical or horizontal—for each polarizer orientation. This distribution is totally discontinuous. Bell's theorem does not apply.

Each and every potential polarization of each photon is determined at the source. The fact that the experimenter does not learn what the result of that determination is until later, when the photons actually arrive at their polarizers, is of no significance.

Delayed rotation of a polarizer is also of no significance. Whatever the orientation of a polarizer when a photon arrives, the polarizer measures the previously determined polarization accordingly.

Because parameters in the source—parameters that are at present unknown—determine the polarization that one will observe at each polarizer orientation, the result of an observation of the polarization of a particular photon with the polarizer at one particular orientation tells one nothing about the polarization that one would have observed for that same particular photon at another polarizer orientation. This is true according to TEW as well as quantum mechanics. The difference is that in TEW, were we able to learn the nature of these parameters in the source and in addition learn their numerical values upon emission of a particular photon, we *would* be able to predict the result of an observation with the polarizer at any orientation. In quantum mechanics, such prediction is impossible in principle.

The Innsbruck experiment does not confirm nonlocality or backwards-in-time causation or any other such nonsense. Einstein's philosophic view was correct. He wins the debate, as if there were ever any logical basis for the opposing view.

Quantum mechanics has not "refuted reality," as if any sane human being would entertain such a claim. What single fact could possibly be supported by more evidence than the fact of reality? Open your eyes and look anywhere; it's all over the place.

6.4 Physics and Metaphysics

Modern physicists frequently claim that any theory purporting to explain a physical phenomenon, as opposed to merely describing the subject behavior mathematically, is necessarily "metaphysical" and therefore scientifically invalid. They claim that in developing quantum mechanics they have risen above such "metaphysical" speculation and have developed a purely empirical, scientific theory. They reject theories such as TEW as having allegedly gone beyond what is observed and as therefore being "metaphysical."

It is true that metaphysical principles do not explain specific physical phenomena. But in branding theories such as TEW as "metaphysical" and quantum mechanics as empirical and scientific, modern physicists have matters exactly backwards.

Modern philosophers conceive of metaphysics as being little more than groundless mysticism. Gone entirely from modern intellectual thought is metaphysics as conceived by Aristotle. Metaphysical principles, properly so-called, are those principles that apply to everything that exists—to reality as such. Aristotle demonstrated how to discern and validate these principles through observation of objects in reality. The principles do not follow from the specific properties of any one object or set of objects but instead are facts observed to be true of objects as such.

An example of a metaphysical principle is the well established fact that when one opens one's eyes and looks, what is there determines what one sees. The act of looking doesn't determine what exists; what exists determines what one sees when one looks. Another metaphysical principle is that a real object can be only what it is, not what it isn't. These principles state in the broadest possible terms the nature of the universe we live in and our relationship, as conscious beings, to that universe.

Such principles might appear so obvious as to be unnecessary, or even useless, to state. However, as described in this and the preceding chapters, modern physicists openly challenge these principles. The Kaiser experiment allegedly demonstrates that subatomic particles exist in no state in particular and that the act of observing a particle puts it into the state observed; looking makes it so. The hypothetical experiment with polarization "boxes" allegedly leads to the same conclusion. The double-slit experiment allegedly demonstrates that each particle goes through both slits and thus has no location in particular until it is observed at the screen. The fact is, quantum mechanics deals with the phenomena in all these experiments by altering the metaphysics—by "twisting reality," as stated in Chapter 1.

TEW, on the other hand, offers a physical explanation for the phenomena. Reciprocal elementary waves are the cause in every case. The phenomena themselves constitute the empirical evidence for the existence of the elementary waves. One might disagree with the conclusion that TEW is the correct explanation, but at least it is a physical explanation. It is quantum mechanics that offers the metaphysical "explanation." Indeed, the essence of what is objectionable about quantum mechanics is precisely its ubiquitous attempts to account for phenomena through metaphysics.

In developing TEW or any other valid physical theory, one must rely on the metaphysical principles just stated, among others. But this doesn't mean that TEW has been deduced from metaphysics. On the contrary, following these principles assures TEW's basis in reality.

Chapter 7

RELATIVITY

7.1 The Velocity of Light

Einstein's theory of relativity has been the source of endless fascination for physicists and non-physicists alike almost from the day of its publication in 1905. Both its precepts and its conclusions appear to be highly counterintuitive, if not in open contradiction with ordinary common sense. Yet nuclear power is a reality; atomic bombs do explode; both were created as the result of relativity theory and in particular as the result of Einstein's famous equation $E=mc^2$.

Because of its counterintuitive nature, modern physicists and philosophers have exploited relativity theory, perhaps even more than quantum mechanics, in their relentless assault on reason and reality. Relativity supposedly proves that "everything is relative;" "my reality is not the same as your reality;" "there is no such thing as objective reality;" etc. Such phrases have become commonplace in today's culture. In fact, relativity provides no valid basis for any such conclusions. Physicists reached these and other equally absurd conclusions by applying to relativity the same faulty methodology that they employed in developing quantum mechanics.

Relativity theory appears to be counterintuitive right from the start with the fundamental physical fact upon which the theory is based, namely, that the velocity of light is always one constant value relative to any observer regardless of the state of motion of that observer. Countless experiments have overwhelmingly confirmed this fact, yet it appears to clash with ordinary experience.

Suppose an observer standing on the side of a road with a radar system measures the speed, or velocity, of an oncoming car as 60 miles per hour. Suppose a police cruiser were approaching from the opposite direction, also at 60 miles per hour, as measured again by the same observer. If the policeman were to measure the velocity of the first car relative to himself by using the cruiser's own radar system, he would see its relative velocity as 120 miles per hour. The motion of the cruiser clearly would affect the velocity of the first car relative to the cruiser. And yet, if the observer on the side of the road and the policeman were both to measure the velocity of the light coming from the first car—the light by virtue of which each observer can see that car—both would get the same result—the same constant value c (as the velocity of light has come to be designated).

The very counterintuitivity of this fact cries out for an explanation. Yet modern physicists, in keeping with their usual procedure, have made no attempt to explain why it is true. Einstein did seek an explanation. He believed (correctly) that the explanation must lie in the nature of light itself; but, as occurred in the case of quantum mechanics, modern physicists in general discounted Einstein's explanatory philosophy and declined to look for the explanation. Einstein correctly developed the mathematical consequences of the fact of the constancy of the velocity of light. Physicists have merely taken Einstein's equations, declared them to directly represent what takes place physically, and concluded that the contradictions that resulted are real.

For example, the equations predict that an object that measures one length when not moving will appear to be shorter when moving rapidly relative to the observer. Modern physicists conclude that the object actually is shorter when in rapid motion—that the object itself physically changes—or at least that it is actually shorter *for that observer*. But, at the same time, to an observer moving with the object, relative to whom the object is not moving, the length of the object *is* unchanged. So the same object is supposedly different in size to different observers—not merely different in appearance or description, but different in fact.

Similarly, clocks appear to run more slowly when in rapid motion, also as predicted by Einstein's equations. Modern physicists claim that the moving clocks actually do run more slowly for the observer at rest, although not for the observer moving with the clock.

Indeed, if two observers are in motion relative to one another, the modern view says that clocks and extended objects moving with observer 2 *are* slower and shorter, respectively, to observer 1, while, simultaneously, clocks and extended objects moving with observer 1 *are* slower and shorter to observer 2.

Even more obviously absurd, if it were the case that one's motion caused other objects to actually change size, this would imply that the act of getting up and walking across the room would cause every object in the entire universe to its farthest reaches to instantly change size and shape. Talk about a nonlocal theory!

An object doesn't change into something else because an observer looks at it differently or moves while looking. The object might *appear to be* different, but it cannot in fact *be* different. A is A. An analogy is the familiar straight stick that looks bent when half under water. The stick isn't actually bent; it only appears to be bent due to the change to the light brought about by refraction at the surface of the water. The same has to be true in the case of objects appearing to be shorter when moving rapidly. Somehow the motion of the observer relative to the object changes the light with which the object is observed.

The light we see consists of particle photons coming from objects to our eyes. There is only one way the motion of those photons could be affected by motion of the observer: Something has to be moving from the observer to the oncoming photons to affect their motion. Fortuitously, we now already know what that "something" is: elementary waves.

According to TEW, any particle that arrives at a detector gets there by following a wave coming from that detector. In the case of observed light, the observer's eye is the "detector." Waves coming from the eye to the observed object stimulate the emission of particle photons. These photons then follow the waves to the eye to produce the visual effect. The waves dictate how the photons move. In particular, the waves determine the velocity of the photons. Because the waves come from the eye and not from the photon source—the source in this case being the object observed—the waves fix the velocity of the photons as c relative to the observer, not relative to the object. Hence the constancy of c relative to the observer. TEW thereby explains the "counterintuitive" constancy of c.

This explanation directly applies only to light that travels over short distances. Light that we see today coming from distant galaxies, for example, was emitted by the galaxy at a time when we didn't yet even exist. Clearly a wave coming from us could not have stimulated the emission of those photons or guided them on most of their journey to our eye. Section 7.2 describes how the above explanation carries over to such long-distance light.

For centuries scientists have gone back and forth as to whether light is a particle or a wave or both, and whether light travels from observer to object or from object to observer. TEW provides the answer: Light consists of both a wave moving from observer to object and a particle moving from object to observer.

Because particle photons, and not the waves, are what produce the visual image, and because they travel from object to observer, numerous experiments have shown that "light" moves from object to observer. During the 19th century, when light was thought to be only a wave, physicists concluded that the wave travels from object to observer. Following Einstein's discovery that light is both a wave and a particle, physicists retained this "forward-wave" view; both the wave and the particle—or perhaps, more accurately, the "wave-particle"—were thought to move from object to observer. This erroneous forward-wave view produces the presumed weirdness in relativity theory just as it does in quantum mechanics.

The forward-wave picture of light makes it impossible to explain the constancy of c. The causal link provided by the reciprocal elementary waves is absent from the picture. Physicists came to view the apparent shrinking of moving objects and slowing of moving clocks as "just the way things are"—as occurring for no reason. Hence the absurd view that a moving object actually does shrink and a moving clock actually does slow down.

While TEW was discovered through examination of the facts described (incorrectly) by quantum mechanics, it might just as well have been discovered from the fact of the constancy of c. As argued above, that constancy demonstrates that something has to be moving "the other way." But TEW would never have been discovered—from quantum mechanics or relativity—had physicists continued to believe that things can happen for no reason.

7.2 Relativistic Effects

Consider the thought experiment pictured in Figure 7.1. An observer on Earth is situated midway between two widely separated lamps. The lamps flash simultaneously. The light from each lamp takes a time to reach the observer, but he sees the two flashes at the same instant, and because he knows the distance to each lamp, and knows the velocity of light c, he determines when the flashes actually took place, and determines in particular that they occurred simultaneously.

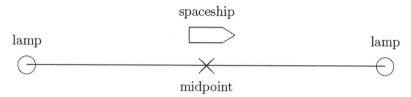

Figure 7.1: Simultaneity Thought Experiment

A second observer passes by in a rapidly moving spaceship traveling in the direction from one lamp to the other. The spaceship arrives next to the midpoint between the lamps at the same instant that the light from the two lamps arrives. What does a passenger in the spaceship see and what does he conclude, as compared with what the observer on Earth thinks the passenger will conclude?

Assuming for the moment the correctness of the ordinary, everyday—pre-relativity—view of space and time, the rider in the spaceship also concludes that the lamps had flashed simultaneously. He sees the light from the two lamps simultaneously, he observes that the light has traveled over the same distance from each lamp and with the same velocity c relative to himself, all just as is the case for the observer on Earth.

The observer on Earth, however, will think that the rider in the spaceship reached an entirely different conclusion. If light moves with velocity c relative to the observer, Earth-man will think that the light observed by space-man coming from the lamp to the rear of the spaceship had moved with velocity $c+v$ where v is the velocity of the spaceship. Earth-man thinks that this light, because it comes from the rear of the spaceship, must be traveling at this higher velocity in order that it be "catching up" to the spaceship at velocity c relative to the spaceship. Likewise, Earth-man would think that light seen by space-man coming from the lamp in front of the spaceship had moved with velocity $c-v$. Earth-man would thus think that space-man would conclude that the lamp in front of the spaceship had flashed first, before the other lamp, this in order that the slower moving light from the lamp in front would have time to arrive at the spaceship at the same instant as the light from the lamp in the rear. Earth-man would think that space-man would conclude that the two flashes—the two instants when the lamps actually flashed, not the instants when the space-man sees the resulting flashes of light—had not occurred simultaneously.

This analysis is, of course, flawed, given that it assumes the correctness of the pre-relativity view of space and time. The analysis refutes its own implicit pre-relativity view of time, in which time is identical at all points in space to all observers regardless of their motion. If what is simultaneous to one observer is not simultaneous to another, this view of time is incorrect. Even though flawed, the analysis nonetheless illustrates why it is that events seen as simultaneous by one observer will (in general) not be seen as simultaneous by another observer in motion relative to the first. It is this change to simultaneity, exacerbated as the clock travels further and further, that makes a rapidly moving clock appear to have slowed down.

The "relativity of simultaneity" makes clear why a moving object appears to be shorter. Imagine attempting to measure the length of a rocket flying overhead. One way of doing this might be to take a photograph of the rocket, use radar or some other means to determine the distance to the rocket, take into account any magnification by the camera, and by measuring the length of the image on the photograph determine the rocket's length. Whether by this method or some other, to measure the rocket's length—other than by contacting someone on the rocket and having them make the measurement—one must determine the location of the front end of the rocket and the location of the back end…simultaneously. Because simultaneity is relative, the length measured by the observer on the ground will not be the same as the length measured by a passenger in the rocket. A passenger in the rocket, if he could determine the exact instants when the observer on the ground looked at the front end and then at the back end, would think that the ground observer had looked at the front end first and only a moment later looked at the back end. Meanwhile, the rocket will have moved, placing the back end closer to the observed position of the front end. Hence to the observer on the ground the rocket will appear to be shorter.

Both the apparent slowing down of rapidly moving clocks and the apparent shortening of rapidly moving objects thus have a straight-forward physical explanation. The mystery disappears. Objects do not actually shrink when they move; they merely appear to shrink, due to the change to the light. Clocks do not actually slow down when they move; they merely appear to slow down.

Einstein's basic relativity equations express quantitatively the re-lationship between lengths of objects and intervals of time as seen by one observer and the corresponding lengths and time intervals as seen by a second observer in motion relative to the first. In current phys-ics terminology, the equations relate events as seen by an observer in one "frame of reference" to the same events as seen by an observer in another "frame of reference." Physicists have produced overwhelming empirical confirmation that the equations accurately describe what occurs in reality.

The mathematical derivation of Einstein's equations is the same in TEW as it is in current theory. Both derivations follow from the same basic fact: the constant value of c relative to all observers. The only dif-ference between the two theories is that TEW *explains* that basic fact, whereas current theory merely assumes it as given. Einstein's equations are thus valid according to TEW just as they are in current theory.

One fact Einstein's equations demonstrate is that an object moving with velocity c relative to one observer will necessarily move with veloc-ity c relative to any other observer regardless of this other observer's state of motion. Photons, in particular, needn't be following an elementary wave from a particular observer in order that they necessarily move with velocity c relative to that observer. An observer, of course, will not actually see photons unless they end up following a wave from that observer; but we can nonetheless refer to the velocity with which they would appear to move were we able somehow to observe them while they were in flight. That velocity will always be *c*. The TEW explanation of relativity for light that travels over short distances thus extends to light traveling over long distances.

7.3 Space and Time

Prior to the discovery of relativity theory, scientists thought that time at any instant was the same at all locations in the universe. Clocks might be set differently at different locations, but all clocks would still be measuring the same time. There would be no relativity of simultaneity or the like. This is generally referred to as a "Galilean" view of time, a view in which time is entirely separate from space and from motion in space.

In addition, in this pre-relativity view, space was viewed as being "absolute." At whatever point in space a particular object was located, that point was that point, and all observers would observe the object as being at that point. If one were to choose a coordinate system in space—an *x, y* and *z* axis relative to which points in the space would be identified—all observers would see space as properly "measured" by that coordinate system. Every object would be located at a definite place in "absolute" space. Such space is also generally referred to as "Galilean." This was Newton's view of space. Relativity theory leads to the conclusion that these Galilean views, both of time and of space, are incorrect. Neither time nor space conform to this view.

Space and time are both concepts, not percepts. We do not perceive either one. What we perceive are objects. We observe that objects can move about and take the place of one another. On this basis we form the concept of space as the place where objects can be. We observe that objects can move at different rates, and on this basis form the concept of time. Time, as defined by Aristotle, is the measure of motion.

All of the observations upon which we base the concepts of space and time are carried out using physical light. Even if we locate an object by touch, we would ultimately use light to locate the hand or other appendage by which we would do the touching. The concepts of space and time cannot be separated from the properties of light. It is for this reason that space and time are necessarily relativistic, or "Lorentzian," and not Galilean.

The fact that space and time are Lorentzian, however, does not imply that space is some sort of real stuff that shrinks or expands as one moves, nor does it imply that objects themselves change when one moves. Modern physicists have arrived at these absurd conclusions because, not having recognized the existence of elementary waves, they were unable to explain relativistic effects. In fact, all that changes when one moves is the light used to observe objects. In no way does relativity imply that any object actually is one thing to one person and something different to someone else. We all see exactly the same objects; A is A.

When one uses coordinate axes to specify locations in space, an axis is not in any sense measuring space. Space, again, is not a thing; it is the place where things can be. A coordinate axis is, in effect, an imaginary measuring tape used to measure the distances between objects. But an actual measuring tape is itself a real object. As such, motion of an observer relative to the tape (and in a direction along the tape's length) will make the tape appear to be shorter. It is not space as such that shrinks as one moves. It is the appearance of the measuring tape that shrinks.

Many attempts have been made to explain relativity. By "explain," the authors of these attempts invariably mean: reduce Lorentzian space and time to Galilean space and time, that is, to an alleged absolute space and time of the universe. In the first place, physicists have conclusively shown that it is impossible to carry out such a reduction in a manner consistent with all of the different experiments performed to test the consequences of relativity. But, more substantively, we have no perceivable basis upon which to form the concept of any such absolute space. At the outset of our knowledge, what we see are real objects, perceived using real light. We have no access to knowledge based on anything else. We never see any object called "space." Space, again, is a *concept*—formed by observing real objects—not a percept.

It is misleading even to state that we live in a Lorentzian universe as opposed to a Galilean universe. The universe does not consist of (Lorentzian or Galilean) space and time with objects added, much like a large room into which objects are placed. We live in a universe of real objects—the objective universe consisting of the objects we perceive—wherein we use light to determine the time and place of events involving those real objects. This requires that our concepts of space and time be

Lorentzian, not that space and time be some sort of real, Lorentzian "stuff," or that space be some sort of room.

In the spaceship thought experiment, when Earth-man concludes that the lamps flashed simultaneously and space-man concludes that they did not, it might appear as if Earth-man was "right" and space-man "wrong." As the experiment is described, the lamps are stationary relative to Earth-man, so one might think that what Earth-man sees is what actually happens, whereas the motion of space-man changes the appearance of this "right" conclusion. Were the two lamps both moving relative to Earth-man, however, the analysis of the situation would remain the same, provided the lamps still flashed at the same time and place relative to Earth-man. Any motion of the lamps is irrelevant. One could reverse the analysis and ask what space-man would think Earth-man had concluded; the result would be the same. Neither observer is "right" and the other "wrong." Each observes the time and place of events relative to themselves. But this does not mean that there is no right answer—that "everything is relative." It is possible to establish the exact relationships between what is observed by each of the two observers only because both are observing exactly the same objects.

Whether it be the stick that looks bent in water or the object that looks shorter when moving rapidly, the fact that the nature of light affects the visual image that our eyes present to our consciousness does not mean that we never see objects as they "really are," whatever than might mean. What we see *is* reality—reality as it really is, if you will. The only alternative would be to see reality as it really isn't. But reality isn't what it isn't. One cannot observe what "isn't." Our senses necessarily convey true information to our consciousness. If a rapidly moving object did *not* appear to be shorter, *that* would be in contradiction with the facts of reality. For our senses to "err," they would necessarily have to violate the laws of physics.

7.4 Relativity Corroborates TEW

The elementary wave theory of subatomic physics and Einstein's theory of relativity are thus not separate theories but in fact are part and parcel of the same single theory. TEW explains the wave-like behaviors of particles, and simultaneously, when applied to photons, explains relativity. TEW is, one might say, "automatically" relativistic—it is already relativistic as it stands.

At least half of a modern day tome on quantum mechanics consists of the analysis by which an initially non-relativistic quantum mechanics is "relativised." Here alone TEW eliminates the need for, or usefulness of, more than half of current quantum theory.

Had Einstein not yet discovered relativity theory, TEW would have predicted it. The fact that TEW, discovered solely on the basis of the wave-like behaviors of particles, predicts and explains relativity theory strongly corroborates TEW as being the correct theory of subatomic phenomena.

7.5 Picture of Elementary Wave Flux

The waves coming from each slit in Figure 2.4 begin at the slit and propagate out from there in all directions. This behavior is characteristic of waves propagating in a medium, or along the surface of a body or water in the case of water waves. Elementary waves do not propagate in a medium. They are "stand-alone" objects in their own right. The elementary wave along a line that a particle might follow moves as a single, independent unit. It might best be described as a "flux" that carries the wave oscillations along with it. The elementary wave previously described as emanating from a detector, or from a point on the screen in the double-slit experiment, and moving out from there in all directions actually consists of an independent flux line along each of the many directions from that detector. The detector gives the independent fluxes a common phase and marker, so they add up to what looks exactly like a wave propagating in all directions, but the individual fluxes are nonetheless independent. The fluxes move with the velocity of light, c.

When an elementary wave flux along a particular line interacts with an elementary particle, the flux does not actually deflect, or scatter, into a new direction. Instead, the interaction connects the initial flux with a second flux already traveling along a different line. Both fluxes continue along their initial line with the same intensity. In the "connection," the phase and "marker" carried by one flux might be passed to the second flux, depending on the nature of the specific interaction; but there is no net increase or decrease in the "quantity" of flux in any direction.

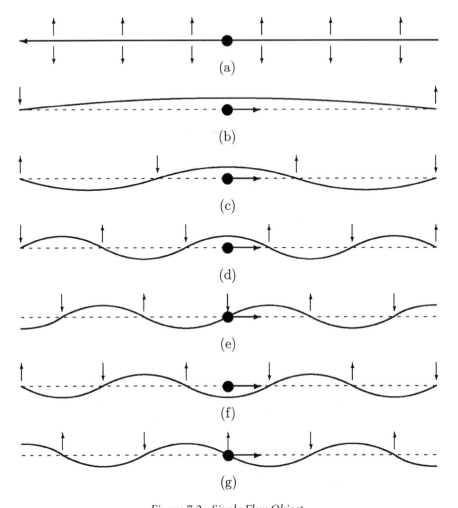

Figure 7.2: Single Flux Object

Consider the flux guiding a particle along a particular line. We know that the flux looks like a wave, at least for a particle in motion. To an observer moving with the particle, however—an observer in the "frame of reference" of the particle—the entire flux object looks like the segment shown in Figure 7.2a. The flux along the line is moving to the left with velocity c and every point along the line is "oscillating" in unison. This picture is in partial agreement with quantum mechanics, in which the quantum wave for a stationary particle looks exactly the same except for the motion of the flux. The "oscillations" are not actually physical motions back and forth but instead represent a periodic variation of a property internal to the flux. The figure shows the periodic variation as a physical oscillation in space solely for representational purposes.

To an observer moving slowly to the left relative to the particle—in a frame of reference in which the particle is moving to the right—the oscillating flux line at a particular point in time might look like Figure 7.2b. The oscillation is at its maximum in the "up" direction at the location of the particle. Because the observer is moving relative to the particle, however, simultaneity will now be different to this observer. Events in front of the particle's motion will appear to occur at a later time, events behind at an earlier time. At the end of the segment in front of the particle, the flux is "moving" up, but it has not yet reached its maximum. The event of reaching its maximum will occur later. At the end of the segment to the rear of the particle, the oscillation has already reached its maximum and is moving down.

From a frame of reference moving more rapidly to the left, the oscillating segment might look like Figure 7.2c. At the front end, the oscillation has not yet even reached the previous minimum, much less the maximum. And so forth along the segment. At the rear, the oscillation has reached its minimum and has started back up toward the next maximum—the maximum prior to the one at the location of the particle. Figure 7.2d shows what might be observed from a still faster moving frame of reference.

Suppose we keep the observer moving at this same faster velocity and record what develops over time. As shown in Figure 7.2d, the front end of the segment was moving up. A moment later it will have reached its maximum, as shown in Figure 7.2e. By the same token, what had been the maximum just to the left is now moving down. What had been the next minimum is now moving up, and so on along the segment.

At a slightly later time, the front end has passed its maximum and is moving down, as shown in Figure 7.2f. And so on through the segment at that time, and likewise at a still later time in Figure 7.2g.

Observe what is happening: The wave "humps" are moving to the right. What was merely a vibration of the whole flux line in unison if viewed from the frame of reference in which the particle was at rest has now taken on the appearance of a traveling wave moving to the right—

moving in the same direction as the particle. The flux itself still moves to the left, where presumably it has stimulated the emission of the particle now following that flux. But the wave oscillations are nonetheless moving to the right.

The wave that "appears" in this manner is identical in appearance to the forward-moving quantum mechanical wave for a particle of identical mass and velocity. Quantitatively, for a particle of mass m, the equation that gives the frequency—the number of oscillations per second—of the flux when viewed from the frame of reference of the particle is

$$\nu = \frac{mc^2}{h}, \tag{7.1}$$

where h again is Planck's constant. Chapter 9 explains the physical origin of this formula. The "period" T of an oscillation—the number of seconds per oscillation—is thus given by

$$T = \frac{1}{\nu} = \frac{h}{mc^2}. \tag{7.2}$$

According to relativity theory, if an observer is moving with velocity v, stationary clocks a distance L in front of it will appear to be ahead by the amount

$$\delta = \frac{Lv}{c^2}. \tag{7.3}$$

In the case of the moving particle following the flux, if the observer is moving with velocity v, the particle is moving with velocity $-v$ relative to the observer; so clocks a distance L in front of the moving particle will appear to the observer to be *behind* by an amount given by equation 7.3.

We can combine these equations to determine the wavelength λ of the wave. The wavelength equals the distance L at which the delay δ in the clock equals the period T for one oscillation:

$$\frac{\lambda v}{c^2} = \frac{h}{mc^2},$$

or, cancelling the c^2 and rearranging,

$$\lambda = \frac{h}{mv} = \frac{h}{p}. \tag{7.4}$$

This is the very famous and well confirmed DeBroglie formula for the wavelength of the wave in terms of the momentum p of the particle following that wave. This confirms that the wave that "appears" in the above TEW-based analysis is quantitatively identical to the corresponding quantum mechanical wave.

We thus have a picture of the elementary wave/flux objects. Every flux line corresponds to a particle at rest in one frame of reference or another, and takes on the appearance of a traveling wave in other frames. The flux moves in the direction opposite to a particle's motion, whereas the wave "humps" move in the same direction as the particle.

The fact that a flux line has no wave in the rest frame but does in a moving frame might make it appear as if the picture contradicts something stated earlier in this chapter, namely, that objects don't change when the motion of the observer changes, that the only change is to the light used to observe objects. After all, many behaviors of the waves result from wave interference, and it appears that there will be none for the rest object.

To see that this is not so, imagine that the wave—when it does look like a wave—travels into a detector that measures its wavelength. This means that the detector simultaneously detects, say, the location of the high point of two successive wave oscillations. Compare this with what would be seen in the frame where the particle is at rest. Here there is no moving wave, but instead the detector is moving toward the particle. Focusing on a particular point along the oscillating wave object, the detector will detect that point as being at one location in the detector at the top of one oscillation and at another location on a successive oscillation, between which detections the detector will have moved. The successive oscillations correspond to the successive wave humps in the first situation, as shown in the discussion of Figure 7.2. The change to the frame of reference does not change the location within each object at which the detections occur. All that has changed is the relative timing and the relative distance between the detections. (And both of these changes are actually changes only to the light waves that might be used in observing the detections.) The rest object acts, in effect, as a wave with an unlimitedly long wavelength.

For that matter, the observer who, in the above analysis, moved in the direction of the flux in order to have the particle and wave move in the opposite direction might just as well have moved in the direction opposite to that of the flux, resulting in the particle and wave moving in the same direction as the flux. In that frame of reference, however, the detector from which the flux is coming will itself be moving in the same direction as the flux and with a large enough velocity that the particle and the detector will still be coming together; the detector will be "catching up" with the particle. The particle still arrives at the detector as before.

TEW's picture of the elementary wave reveals a crucial physical fact: The wave—not the flux, but the wave that "appears" to the moving observer—carries no "signal." The wave does not actually propagate, in the usual meaning of this term. A wave propagates through a medium because the motion of one element of the medium causes the motion of the next element, which causes the motion of the next element, and so on through the medium. The wave that appears on the elementary wave flux is solely the result of the synchronous oscillation of the entire flux as viewed in the rest frame of the particle that would follow that flux. The only physical "signal" involved is that carried by the flux itself, moving with velocity c in the direction opposite to the particle's motion.

These facts resolve another difficulty in the quantum mechanical picture: The velocity of the wave—the velocity with which each "hump" travels—is greater than the velocity of light. In the TEW picture, nothing is actually traveling at that velocity. All that has happened is that clocks are synchronized differently in a moving frame, making it appear as if a wave were propagating with velocity greater than c. In quantum mechanics, the individual waves do propagate with a velocity greater than c, violating relativity theory. Modern physicists try to escape this difficulty by claiming that a particle moves at the "group velocity" of the set of waves making up the "wave-particle." The group velocity is the velocity of a "wave-packet" such as that described in Chapter 5. The group velocity is less than c. But how can this combining of the waves resolve the contradiction if the individual waves making up the combination are nonetheless still traveling with a velocity greater than c? The formulas "work", but the implied physical picture is clearly false.

Chapter 8

PARTICLE "DIFFRACTION"

8.1 Single-Crystals

One of the more dramatic displays of the wave-like behavior of particles is the phenomenon physicists refer to as particle "diffraction."

Physicists have performed experiments in which particles are fired into solid material, the particles scatter off the atoms making up the solid, and some scatter back out of the solid and strike a photographic plate that records their points of impact. Physicists gather information about the solid from the pattern formed on the plate by the scattered particles.

For most solids, the scattered particles form a largely random pattern. But for solids referred to as "single-crystals," physicists find that many of the particles scatter out in a few well defined directions. Figure 8.1 represents what physicists refer to as a "Laue pattern" formed by the scattering of X-rays—high energy photons—by a single-crystal of silicon.

When most materials solidify, the atoms or molecules attach to one another in a very regular pattern, determined by the structure of the electron levels in the atoms or molecules involved. A solid with such a regular pattern of atoms or molecules is termed a "crystal" of that material. Most materials solidify into millions of tiny little crystallites attached to one another in random relative orientations. The regular pattern is formed within each little crystallite, but the pattern doesn't carry over to other neighboring crystallites.

Scientists have, however, devised methods to cause materials to solidify into a single large crystal, reflecting the same pattern through-

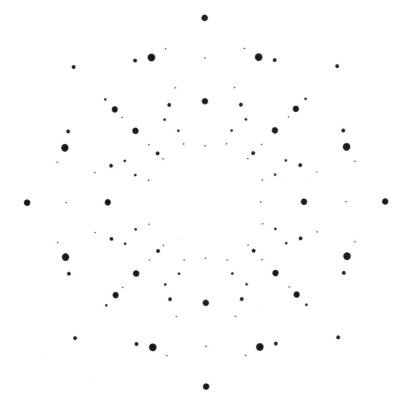

Figure 8.1: Laue Pattern of Silicon

out. Such an object is termed a "single crystal." Diamonds are examples of single crystals that form naturally, in this case single-crystals of carbon.

8.2 Quantum Mechanical Picture of "Diffraction"

Figure 8.2 provides a two-dimensional representation of a simple single crystal. The dots represent the positions of the individual atoms. One can visualize the atoms as being arranged in planes stacked on one another. The horizontal dashed lines connecting the atoms represent one particular set of such planes. Also shown in the figure are lines representing two paths that particles and waves might take in traveling into the crystal and scattering back out. The arrows indicate the direction of motion of the particles. Assume that the particles employed in this example are electrons.

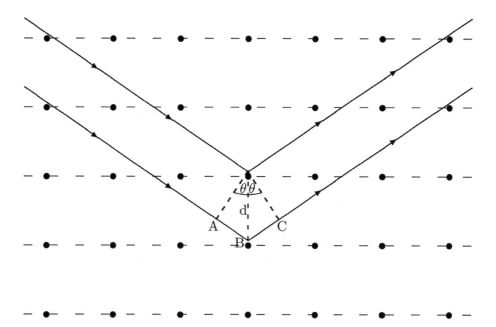

Figure 8.2: Single-Crystal Diffraction

As always, the behavior of the electrons is determined by waves. According to quantum mechanics, the waves originate at the electron source. Each individual atom in the crystal scatters the waves, but the planes will frequently act, in effect, as partial reflectors, with each plane reflecting a small portion of the incoming wave while transmitting most of it to the next plane.

Under most circumstances, a wave reflected by one plane will not end up being in phase with waves reflected by other planes. The waves scattered by the various planes will thus interfere destructively with one another, resulting in little or no net reflected wave.

If, however, the combination of the wavelength of the wave, the separation between the planes, and the angle of reflection satisfies a special condition, the waves reflected from all planes will be in phase with one another, and a strong reflected wave will form. That special condition is illustrated in Figure 8.2. The length of the lower wave path is longer than the upper path by the distance from A to B to C. If that length exactly equals an integral number of wavelengths of the wave, then, while the wave on the lower path will be that same number of wavelengths behind the wave on the upper path after both have been reflected, the two will nonetheless end up exactly in phase with one another. Clearly under these circumstances, the wave reflected off every plane will be in phase with those reflected off every other plane.

Mathematically, the special condition occurs when

$$n\lambda = 2d\sin\theta, \tag{8.1}$$

where n is the number of wavelengths fitting in the length A to B to C, λ is the wavelength of the waves, d is the distance between the two planes, and θ is the angle shown in the figure. In this formula, the $2d\sin\theta$ on the right equals the length from A to B to C.

Wave scattering off successive planes and adding together as described here is known as "Bragg scattering," first discovered by the physicists W. H. and W. L. Bragg in 1913, using X-rays as the scattering particles. Equation 8.1 is known as Bragg's law.

The quantum mechanical picture of this phenomenon leads to the by-now-familiar problems. The electrons are particles when emitted and they are particles when they are observed after leaving the crystal. Yet clearly the scattering is that of a wave. It is specifically wave interference that leads to equation 8.1. But, just as in the double slit, because the wave interference is occurring while the electrons are scattering, no theory in which the electrons follow the wave—and assuming only a local interaction between the electron and the wave—can possibly account for what is observed. Quantum mechanics necessitates the acceptance of "wave-particles," nonlocal interactions, or something equally nonsensical.

According to quantum mechanics, an individual electron doesn't scatter off any one plane in the crystal but instead scatters off all planes simultaneously. Experiments such as this allegedly prove that the particle is a wave while interacting with the crystal.

8.3 The TEW Explanation

As always in TEW, the waves are moving in the opposite direction—from the photographic plate to the electron source. They start as waves, scatter as waves, and leave the crystal as waves. The waves travel to the electron source where they stimulated the emission of the electrons. All wave interference takes place before the electrons are emitted. The electrons then follow the waves by one path or another to the photographic plate. Because the probability of the entire process has already been determined at the electron source, it makes no difference to the outcome which path an individual electron takes. Each electron scatters off only one of the planes. Only the waves scatter off all the atomic planes.

In the experiment that resulted in the X-ray photograph shown in Figure 8.1, X-ray elementary waves were being emitted by all points on the photographic plate. Only the waves originating at the location of one of the bright spots on the photograph satisfied the condition of equation 8.1, so only those waves were scattered toward the X-ray particle source, thereby stimulating the emission of the X-rays, which X-rays then followed the wave back to the photographic plate and formed the bright spot. Waves coming from the blank areas in the photograph didn't satisfy Bragg's law in their scattering and hence interfered destructively at the X-ray particle source, so no X-rays were emitted in response to them, none followed the waves back, and none reached the photographic plate.

Strictly speaking, the particles do not "diffract." "Diffraction" is a term referring to wave interference effects. Only the elementary waves diffract; the particles then follow the waves. Waves are waves, and particles are particles.

Chapter 9

CLASSICAL MECHANICS

9.1 Hamilton-Jacobi Theory

During the 18th and especially the 19th century, physicists proposed numerous methods for solving complex problems in mechanics. Although ultimately based on and validated by Newton's laws of motion, a number of these methods involved somewhat radical reformulations of the mathematical statement of those laws.

One such method, referred to today as "Hamilton-Jacobi theory" (H-J theory), pictures the mechanics of a particle as a particle-follows-wave process. When a particle moves from point A to point B under the influence of various forces, the H-J method, instead of treating the forces as applying directly to the particle as in the Newtonian picture, views the forces instead as acting on a wave moving from A to B. As it propagates, this wave forms a series of wavefronts, as illustrated in Figure 9.1. One can picture the wavefronts as the lines along wave

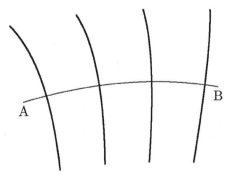

Figure 9.1: Hamilton-Jacobi Theory

crests at a particular point in time. The particle then follows a line that is perpendicular to each of these wavefronts, illustrated by the thinner line in the figure.

Hamilton and Jacobi derived the equation by which one would have to describe the wave if a particle following that wave were to act in accordance with the laws of Newtonian mechanics. It turns out that the "Hamilton-Jacobi equation" so derived is mathematically equivalent to the Schrödinger equation of quantum mechanics when the latter equation is restricted to describing waves only of very short wavelength. As mathematicians would express the relationship, the H-J equation is equivalent to the Schrödinger equation "in the limit as the wavelength goes to zero."

Recall the relationship $p = \dfrac{h}{\lambda}$. Very small wavelength λ corresponds to particles of large momentum p—large, that is, in comparison with Planck's constant h which characterizes the "size" of processes at a subatomic level. Such large momenta are characteristic of macroscopic entities.

Because TEW makes the same predictions as quantum mechanics, the latter being governed by the Schrödinger equation, TEW in the short wavelength limit makes the same predictions as H-J theory. In fact, provided one reverses the direction of the H-J wave to travel from B to A as does the elementary wave, TEW virtually *is* the H-J theory. According to the H-J equation, an H-J wave propagating from B to A under the influence of the same physical forces that effect a wave from A to B will produce the very same wavefronts, although those wavefronts will be moving in the opposite direction. So the motion of a particle following a line perpendicular to the wavefronts will be unchanged by the reversal of the wave. Short-wavelength TEW and H-J are virtually the same theory.

All of "classical," Newtonian mechanics is captured by the H-J theory. TEW thus explains not only the behaviors of subatomic particles but the laws of classical physics as well.

9.2 Where Are the Waves in Newton's Laws?

Behaviors that are specific to subatomic physics as opposed to classical, macroscopic physics are those resulting from wave interference. It is wave interference that leads to the wave-like appearance of the pattern formed on the screen in the double-slit experiment, for example. Wave interference restricts the scattering of particles by single crystals to certain sharply defined angles of scattering. Because waves taking multiple paths can interfere with one another at a particle source, the behavior of a particle can depend on what occurs over those multiple paths.

It is precisely these interference-dependent behaviors that disappear as wavelengths become smaller and smaller. Compare Figure 9.2 with Figure 2.4 in Chapter 2. Figure 9.2 is identical to the earlier figure except for the fact that the wavelength has been cut in half—the separations between the wave crests have become half as large. As a result, the directions in which the wave intensity is a maximum or minimum are closer together. Points such as A and B in Figure 2.4 are roughly half as far apart in Figure 9.2. Clearly, as the wavelength becomes still smaller, the maxima and minima will come even closer together, until at near-zero wavelength the maxima and minima would effectively merge, and the effects of interference would disappear.

In this short-wavelength limit, particles penetrating a slit in the double-slit experiment would no longer scatter preferentially in some directions rather than others. Instead of the wave-like interference pattern formed with longer wavelength waves, the pattern on the screen

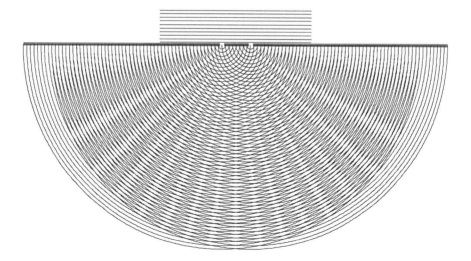

Figure 9.2: Shorter Wavelength Interference

would become relatively uniform. For wavelengths small compared to the width of a slit, the pattern would approach that of Figure 2.2. Under these circumstances, if the only objective were to describe a particle's behavior—in this case the probability that it will reach one point or another on the screen—it would no longer be necessary to include the effect of a wave penetrating both slits. It therefore becomes possible—again, purely for the purpose of describing behavior—to dispense with the wave altogether and develop a formalism in which the particle interacts directly with the edges of the one slit through which it travels or simply passes through the one slit without interaction. The formalism that results is Newtonian mechanics.

The fact that one can, for the purpose of describing behavior, dispense with the wave does not mean that the wave no longer exists, nor that it exists but no longer affects the particle. At short wavelengths, the wave is still penetrating both slits and the particle is still following the wave; but the effects of the interference on the particle's motion become negligible. At a small enough wavelength, the scattering of the wave by a slit will be so negligible that the area on the screen from which waves penetrating one slit will impact the source will lie entirely outside the corresponding area for the other slit. Indeed, one might completely cover the second slit and the behavior of a particle penetrating the first would be unaffected. Even then, however, the particle would still be following the wave penetrating the one slit.

Hamilton and Jacobi did not propose their theory as an attempt to explain the classical laws of motion or even to provide a picture of the physics behind those laws. They proffered their theory merely as a formalism that "works." In fact, the theory comes very close to picturing what actually occurs physically.

The philosophy maintaining that physics must consist only of a mathematical description of behavior that "works" actually became generally accepted long before the advent of quantum mechanics. It already controlled the thinking of physicists at the time of the discovery of subatomic particles. Had physicists been seeking explanations for the behavior they observed instead of merely seeking behavioral formalisms, then when, in the early 20th century, they became aware of the overtly wave-like behavior of subatomic particles, their first thought would have been: H-J theory. But for their anti-explanatory, anti-causal, anti-reality philosophy, they might have discovered the elementary waves at that time and avoided the entire calamitous, incomprehensible, truly insane imbroglio known as quantum mechanics.

Many modern physicists will state explicitly that it makes no difference what philosophy is applied in doing research, just so long as one can get "results." Clearly those physicists are very sadly mistaken.

9.3 Frequency Explains Mass

The physical concepts of mass, momentum and energy arose in the context of classical, Newtonian physics. These concepts identify aspects of the description as to how macroscopic objects behave while interacting with their environment. But because Newtonian physics is, as indicated above, based on an "artificial" picture that omits the waves which actually govern the behaviors of objects, the concepts themselves are, in that sense, artificial. They do not correspond in any direct manner with what actually takes place physically in the processes they are intended to describe.

And yet, far from reformulating Newtonian mechanics with a dynamics based on wave concepts, modern physicists formulate quantum mechanics in terms of the concepts of Newtonian mechanics. In their giant mathematical formalism, Newtonian mechanics came first, so the quantum mechanical formalism is built up from that. Physicists have developed an enormously complicated, yet totally arbitrary and useless, mathematical procedure known as "canonical quantization," by which they take the laws of classical physics and "quantize" them to obtain quantum mechanics. They believe, in effect, that Newtonian physics explains quantum mechanics, not the reverse.

Some examples illustrate how it is that simple wave concepts explain behaviors currently attributed to mass, momentum and energy. Consider again the "diffraction" of particles by single-crystals, as described in Chapter 8. The condition for the preferred scattering is illustrated in Figure 8.1 and is described mathematically in equation 8.1. Consider the situation in which only one wavelength fits in the distance A to B to C, so that $n=1$ in equation 8.1. That equation now reads,

$$\lambda = 2d \sin \theta. \tag{9.1}$$

Using the by now familiar equation,

$$p = \frac{h}{\lambda},\tag{9.2}$$

Equation 9.1, after some rearrangement, becomes

$$2p\sin\theta = \frac{h}{d}.\tag{9.3}$$

Speaking in Newtonian terms, $2p\sin\theta$ is the change in the momentum of a particle of momentum p when deflected as shown in Figure 8.1. Consider then a second particle following a wave with a wavelength half as large. Equation 9.1 then says that the quantity $2\sin\theta$ will be half as large, since d remains unchanged. Equation 9.2 says that the momentum p will be twice as large. The quantity $2p\sin\theta$ will thus remain unchanged, as, according to equation 9.3, it should; h and d are both constants, assuming the same single-crystal. So, as the momentum of the particle changes, the angle of deflection θ changes in just such a manner that the crystal—which has not changed—always imparts the same change in momentum to the particle. The motion of the particle changes in just such a manner as to conserve momentum.

But it is not conservation of momentum that causes particles to obey these relationships when they scatter. Equation 9.1 isn't true because momentum is conserved; it is true as the consequence of interference of the elementary waves. At least for this special case, wave interference *explains* the law of conservation of momentum, not the other way around.

Because in Newtonian mechanics the momentum of a particle is equal to its mass m times its velocity v, or

$$p = mv,$$

the analysis just presented, in which the momentum of a particle is doubled, remains the same whether the velocity is doubled with the mass remaining the same or the mass is doubled while the velocity remains the same. But according to equation 7.1, doubling the mass means doubling the frequency of the wave that the particle follows when viewed in the frame of reference in which the particle is at rest. Equation 7.1 led to equation 7.4, which is merely a different form of equation 9.2. So the choice of equation 7.1 as the relationship between a particle's mass and the frequency of its wave again makes the behaviors predicted by Newtonian mechanics identical to those predicted by TEW.

But, as before, equation 7.1 does not dictate the frequency that the wave corresponding to a particle of mass m must have; it indicates the reverse: The concept "mass" must be defined by equation 7.1 if the resulting Newtonian mechanics is to make correct predictions. Mass is the "artificial" concept defined so that the equations "work." Frequency is the objective concept describing an elementary wave. The elementary waves explain why those equations work. Equation 7.1 should be written:

$$m = \frac{h\nu}{c^2}.$$
(9.4)

The relationship between the energy E of a particle and the frequency ν of the wave that the particle follows is given by the Einstein equation

$$E = h\nu.$$

Substituting E for $h\nu$ in equation 9.4 yields

$$E = mc^2.$$

This famous equation, first written down by Einstein, does not in any way imply that mass is some sort of "fuel" that can be "burned" to create energy, or the like. In fact, written in the Einsteinian form, the physical basis of the relationship is totally opaque. This relationship becomes physically transparent as soon as one recognizes that $E = h\nu$ and $m = \frac{h\nu}{c^2}$.

The primary causative parameters, both in classical physics and in subatomic physics, are the frequency ν and the wavelength λ. The quantities energy, momentum and mass are really nothing more than the artificial parameters related to the frequency and wavelength through the above relationships, relationships chosen so that the resulting Newtonian laws of motion will reproduce the observed behavior—behavior that is actually caused by the waves and their interactions.

When the classical concepts were first defined, scientists did not have knowledge of TEW, or even of quantum mechanics. Given that the laws of motion were initially discovered solely through observation of the mechanical behavior of objects, and given that those laws had not yet been explained, the basic concepts should have been defined solely in terms of that behavior. Newton was mistaken when he defined mass as the "quantity of matter." But now that the laws have been explained, those concepts should be defined, as in the above equations, in terms of the nature of the underlying causative objects—the elementary waves.

Chapter 10

MAGNETISM

10.1 The Magnetic "Field"

The view that physics can be nothing more than a mathematical description of behavior was prevalent well before the 20th century and the advent of quantum mechanics. Physicists, even in the "classical" era, frequently treated objects as if they consisted of their behavior. Indeed, physicists came to create entirely new "objects" consisting of observed behavior, objects sometimes bearing little or no resemblance to the real objects underlying that behavior. Perhaps the worst example of such behavior reification lies in the classical concept of the magnetic "field."

Everyone is familiar with magnets. They pull on metallic objects and push and pull on one another. These pushes and pulls occur even when the magnet is not in direct contact with the object on which it pushes or pulls. In their efforts to describe these behaviors, physicists developed the notion of a magnetic "field," analogous to the earlier notions of gravitational and electric "fields." The magnetic field at any point in space is defined as the force that would be exerted on a unit-sized magnetic pole place at that point. Physicists conceive of the "field" as consisting of the force it is capable of exerting. They frequently refer to gravitational, electric and magnetic fields as "behavioral fields."

But how can any object or "thing" consist of its behavior? The concept of "behavior" presupposes the existence of the object that behaves. Treating a behavioral field as an object assumes that behavior can exist "by itself," not as behavior of anything, just behavior—of nothing.

It is perfectly scientific, of course, to measure the size of the pushes and pulls that a magnet will exert at various points around the magnet and from this to write down equations describing what is observed. This is one of the first steps a scientist would take in seeking to understand the phenomenon. But, much as occurred with quantum mechanics, physicists never went beyond this point to discover the nature of the real objects producing the magnetic forces. The magnetic field itself became the "real" object. Physicists to this day treat electric and magnetic fields as if they were the actual players involved in the phenomena of electricity and magnetism, despite substantial evidence proving that such a picture of things could not possibly be correct.

Perhaps more than any other single factor, it is this notion of disembodied behavior that renders physics so incomprehensible to beginning students of the subject. First comes the concept of "mass," presented as if it were an actual something yet "consisting" of nothing more than the behavior it supposedly describes. But then, worst of all, comes the concept of a behavioral field. The notion of disembodied behavior is, in fact, inconceivable. It should be no surprise that students cannot conceive of it.

10.2 Evidence Contradicting the Field Picture

An enormous quantity of experimental evidence contradicts the reified field picture of magnetism. Consider first the alleged magnetic field of a loop of wire carrying an electric current, as illustrated in two dimensions in Figure 10.1. It is well known that the motion of electrical charges, such as the motion of electrons in an electric current, generates magnetic effects. The motion of an electron circling a nucleus in an atom acts, in effect, as a little current loop and generates magnetic effects. The magnets of everyday experience consist of atoms that have been aligned with one another such that the magnetic effects of the individual atoms add together.

The "lines of force" or "field lines" shown in Figure 10.1 indicate the alleged magnetic field. They indicate the direction of the magnetic "push" that the "field" would exert on a magnetic pole placed at any specific point. It is well established, however, that nothing actually travels along any of these lines. When the current in the loop is first turned on, magnetic effects travel in all directions radially outward from the loop with the velocity of light. The distance from the loop to a neighboring

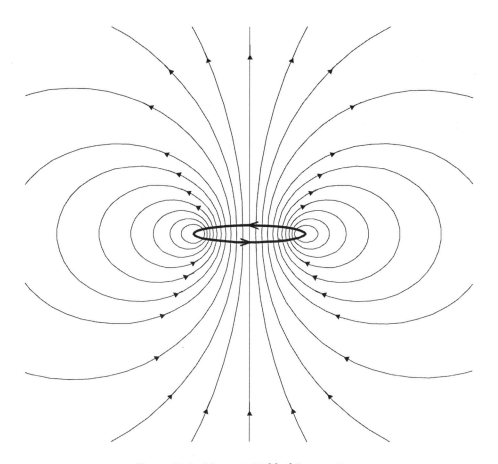

Figure 10.1: Magnetic Field of Current Loop

point measured along a curved field line is necessarily longer than the distance along a straight, radial line from the loop to that point. Anything traveling along a curved field line would thus have to travel much faster than the speed of light were it to arrive at any point away from the loop at the same time that the magnetic effect arrives. Such faster-than-light motion would violate Einstein's theory of relativity. The field lines cannot possibly exhibit the motion of anything real. Few physicists would disagree with this conclusion.

A single moving charge allegedly generates a magnetic field. Yet, at the same time, to an observer moving with the charge—to an observer relative to whom the charge is not moving—there is no magnetic field.

To one observer a field exists; to another observer no field exists. Were an observer who was initially stationary relative to the charge suddenly to move, a magnetic field would allegedly spring into existence, even though nothing had actually been done to the charge or its surroundings; all that had happened was that the observer moved.

The "field" theory says, furthermore, that even when there is a magnetic field at a particular location, the field won't affect a charge at that location unless the charge is itself moving. If an observer is stationary relative to a charge, a magnetic field won't affect the charge. But if the observer moves—so that the charge is now moving relative to the observer—suddenly the magnetic field affects the charge. According to this theory, then, an observer—even one located at a remote distance from a charge—can cause the effect of a magnetic field to switch on and off merely by moving!

Chapter 7 described the fact that objects will appear to be different to observers moving relative to one another. Einstein's equations describe how to "transform" the time and place of events as seen by one observer into the time and place of the same events as seen by another observer. These equations clearly must apply to any and all real phenomena. Yet they do not apply in the case of electric and magnetic fields. Given the manner in which physicists define the electric and magnetic fields, they are forced to use a special transformation in which electric and magnetic fields transform into one another to make the net effect of the two transformed fields conform to observation. So the electric and magnetic "fields" cannot be picturing what actually exists. If they did, they would transform according to Einstein's equations in the same manner as any other real phenomenon.

The combination of the electric and magnetic fields, including their alleged transformation into one another, does transform correctly. Physicists have recognized that electric and magnetic effects are aspects of the behavior of a single "electromagnetism." They still persist, however, in describing that electromagnetism as if it consisted of the separate electric and magnetic fields.

The contradictions of the magnetic field picture reached a quantum mechanical level of absurdity with the discovery of what is known as the "Aharanov-Bohm effect." Without going into details, it is alleged that, in the circumstances of this effect, a magnetic field affects subatomic particles even when the particles never come into contact with that field. The field allegedly produces effects even at locations where there is no field. The field object, consisting of its behavior, behaves where it doesn't behave! Yet modern physicists go right on with the magnetic field picture. After all, the formulas "work."

10.3 Vecton Theory of Electromagnetism

Simply by applying the principle that behavior is necessarily behavior of something, and by remembering the principles of TEW, the correct theory of magnetism falls into place almost effortlessly.

Just as they attribute magnetic effects to a behavioral magnetic field, physicists attribute the electrical forces between charged particles to a behavioral electric field. Figure 10.2 illustrates the alleged electric field of a single positively charged particle at rest relative to the observer. At every point around the particle an electrical force would be exerted on a second positively charged particle placed at the point, with the force pointing directly away from the first charge as shown. Some particles are charged positively, some negatively. The alleged field of the positive charge in Figure 10.2 would attract a negative charge. A negative charge

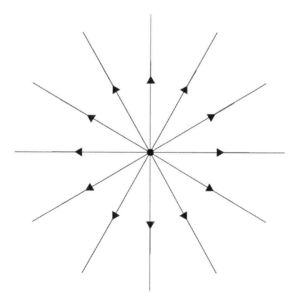

Figure 10.2: Electric Field of Positive Charge

allegedly emits an electric field that will attract positive charges and repel negative charges. Like charges repel, opposites attract.

As with magnetism, the electrical effects of a charged particle travel radially outward from the particle with the velocity of light. The pattern of the electric field "lines" suggests that the charge is continually emitting numerous very small objects, which travel along straight lines away from the charge until they encounter a second charge and produce the force on that second charge. For reasons that will become clear in a moment, suppose we call these small objects "vectons." A charged particle emits vectons in response to the stimulation of vecton elementary waves that impinge on the charged particle.

First of all, because particles can be either positive or negative, vectons must have the capability either to "push" or "pull" on a charge upon impacting it, depending on its charge. So vectons cannot be described as carrying "momentum," which would then be transferred to a second charge when the vecton "runs into it," so to speak; the momentum of a particle necessarily points in the direction in which the particle is moving. Vectons must carry an internal property of some kind by virtue of which they impart a "jolt" to an absorbing particle along a direction determined by this internal property, not by the direction in which the vecton is moving. A mechanical analogy would be that the vecton carries a small device that explodes upon impact, sending a jolt in a direction determined by the placement of the device. The various objects making up any real mechanical device would, of course, interact so as to conserve momentum, so this is at best an analogy.

Imagine, then, that a vecton carries a little "push-vector" pointing in a direction determined by the inner structure of the vecton. A vecton "jolts" a positive charge in the direction of that push-vector, a negative charge in the opposite direction. Suppose in addition that, when a vecton is viewed from the frame of reference of the emitting charge, the push-vector of a vecton emitted by a positive charge—a positive vecton—points along its direction of motion, whereas the push-vector of a vecton emitted by a negative charge—a negative vecton—points in the opposite direction.

While a positive vecton points along its direction of motion when viewed in the frame of reference of the charge that emitted it, such will no longer be the case when the vecton is observed from a frame of reference moving relative to the charge. Consider an analogy from everyday experience: Joe Namath[1] is riding in a convertible. He throws a pass directly to the side of the moving car. Relative to Mr. Namath, the car is, of course, not moving. Relative to the car—and because, being Joe Namath, the pass will be a perfect spiral—the football moves as shown in the left-hand portion of Figure 10.3. The oval-shaped football "points" directly along the line of motion of the football itself.

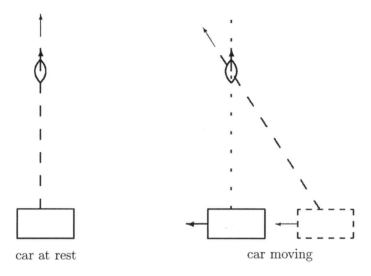

car at rest   car moving

Figure 10.3: Joe Namath Effect

Relative to an observer standing on the side of the road, however, the football's motion is as shown in the right-hand portion of Figure 10.3. The motion of the car makes the football follow a path at some acute angle to the road. The football's oval, however, is still pointing in the same direction—directly away from Namath. So, to the roadside observer, the long axis of the football no longer points in the same direction as the ball's motion. The direction of the ball's "point" appears to be rotated.

Because the push-vector of a vecton is, like the long-axis "point" of the football, an internal property of the vecton, an observer moving

---

[1] Joe Namath is an American football legend. His five touchdown passes led the New York Jets to victory in the first Super Bowl.

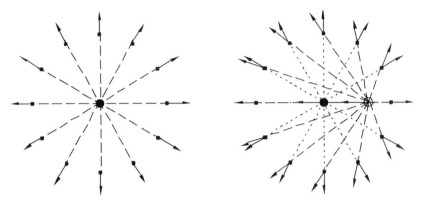

Figure 10.4: Vecton Emission

relative to the charge that emitted the vecton will see the push-vector as similarly rotated. Figure 10.4 illustrates vectons emitted by a positive charge. The left side of the Figure shows a charged particle at rest, the right side a charged particle in motion to the left. For the particle in motion, the dashed lines are the paths of motion of the vectons, the dotted lines the vecton paths that would have been observed had the charge been stationary at its leftmost position. The vecton push-vectors are directed along the latter lines. The push-vectors of the vectons emitted by the moving charge appear to be rotated. (Figure 10.4 is quantitatively inaccurate in that it doesn't show the effects of relativity on the motions of the vectons.)

Because the vectons with push-vectors appear to correspond in a simple manner to the electric field of a stationary charge, as shown in Figure 10.2, it is tempting to conclude that electric effects are the direct result of the push-vectors while magnetic effects result from the fact that the push-vectors are rotated. However, as an example will demonstrate, when charged particles are in motion, there is, in general, no such simple correspondence between the vecton theory and the separate electric and magnetic fields of current theory. The vecton theory does, however, reproduce the combined effects of the alleged electric and magnetic fields.

10.4 Forces Between Current Carrying Wires

An electrical wire consists of atoms with relatively fixed positions within the wire, some of whose electrons have been released and are free to move about within the wire. An electric current consists of motion of these free electrons along the wire.

Physicists have determined that two current carrying wires exert forces on one another. According to current theory, these forces are produced by magnetic fields. The motion of the electrons in each segment of one wire allegedly produces a magnetic field at the location of each segment of the second wire. This magnetic field in turn allegedly exerts forces on the moving electrons making up the current in the second wire, thus producing the force between the wires.

The charged particles in each wire exert electric forces on the charged particles of the second wire at all times, with or without a current in the wires. These forces are allegedly produced by the electric fields which the various charged particles allegedly emit. But these forces balance out. The electrons in wire 1 exert a repulsive force on the electrons in wire 2, but simultaneously exert an equal and opposite attractive force on the positive nuclei in wire 2. Similarly, the positive nuclei in wire 1 exert a balancing attractive and repulsive force on wire 2's electrons and nuclei, respectively. Current theory maintains that these specifically electric forces balance out even when the negative electrons are in motion—even when there is an electrical current in both wires. Any attraction between the wires is, again, allegedly produced solely by the alleged magnetic fields.

Consider two parallel current carrying wires as shown in Figure 10.5, and consider in particular the force between a small segment of one wire and the closest neighboring similar small segment in the second

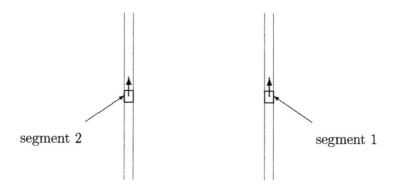

Figure 10.5: Segments of Parallel Wires

wire. First of all, if only, say, wire 1 carried a current, then even if the moving electrons constituting that current were to produce forces on the particles of wire 2 that differed from the forces that they would produce were the electrons stationary, the change would affect the electrons and the nuclei in wire 2 equally and oppositely. No net force between the wires would result. Only if both wires carry a current would any change to the forces produce a net attraction or repulsion between the wires.

When both wires carry a current, the present theory says that if the electrons in the wire 1 segment repel the electrons in the wire 2 segment with an electric force F_{elec}, then the magnetic force F_{mag} between the two wire segments would be given by[2]

$$F_{mag} = -F_{elec} \cdot \frac{v^2}{c^2}, \qquad (10.1)$$

where v is the velocity of the electrons as they move along the wires and c is, again, the velocity of light. (This relationship is true only for the particular orientation of the two segments specified in the example of Figure 10.5.) The minus sign indicates that the alleged magnetic force pushes in the direction opposite to the alleged electric force—the alleged magnetic force between the moving electrons is attractive. The net force F between the moving electrons is thus given by

$$F = F_{elec} + F_{mag} = F_{elec} \cdot \left(1 - \frac{v^2}{c^2}\right). \qquad (10.2)$$

The motion of the electrons reduces the force between them by the factor $\left(1 - \frac{v^2}{c^2}\right)$.

Whatever physical process produces the force between the electrons when they are at rest, however, relativity theory alone dictates that the force will be reduced by this factor $\left(1 - \frac{v^2}{c^2}\right)$ when the electrons are in motion. If the electrons in each wire were free to move away from each other—in a direction perpendicular to each wire—instead of being confined to the wire, the electric force between them would produce an acceleration of each charge away from the other. If the acceleration had value a_0 when the charges were initially at rest, then when the charges are in motion with velocity v along each wire, relativity theory dictates

---

[2] John David Jackson, *Classical Electrodynamics*, Wiley, New York (1962), Chap. 5, Sect. 5.2.

that the acceleration a_{mov} that they would produce in each other—still in a direction perpendicular to the wire—would be given by[3]

$$a_{mov} = a_0 \cdot \left(1 - \frac{v^2}{c^2}\right). \qquad (10.3)$$

This relation is true regardless of the physical cause of the acceleration a_0. Merely by taking the acceleration that exists when the electrons are not moving and asking what that same acceleration would look like from a frame of reference in which the electrons are moving, relativity predicts this result. But reducing the acceleration by the factor $\left(1 - \frac{v^2}{c^2}\right)$ is equivalent to reducing the force of repulsion between the electrons by the same factor, thus explaining the "magnetic" attraction between the wires.

But this is an amazing result! Whatever produces the electric forces between the electrons when they are at rest, *the change to those forces due to relativity theory alone fully explains the allegedly magnetic forces between the wire segments.* There is no new magnetic "stuff" emitted by the moving electrons. Not merely is there no object in reality looking like the magnetic field, no specifically magnetic object of any kind exists at all!

Ironically, current theory says that the alleged electric field at the location of an electron in wire 2, emitted by an electron in wire 1, is reduced by the same factor of $\left(1 - \frac{v^2}{c^2}\right)$ when the electron in wire 1 is in motion with velocity v.[4] Current theory, however, also says that the effect of this change to the electric field applies equally and oppositely to the nuclei and the electrons in wire 2, even when the latter electrons are moving.[5] The altered electric field produces no net force between the wires.

Whatever the error in current theory, this proves that the "electric" forces between stationary charges cannot possibly be the product of any object looking like the electric field. To be compatible with relativity, whatever process produces the forces between the various charged

---

[3] Ibid., p. 388, exercise 11.4.

[4] L. Landau and E. Lifshitz, *The Classical Theory of Fields*, Addison-Wesley, Reading, Mass. (1952), p. 177, Eqn. 8-20.

[5] John David Jackson, op. cit., p. 191, Eqn. 6.87.

particles must transform under relativity so as to account for the repulsion between the current carrying wires. The force allegedly produced by the electric field does not so transform—as stated earlier, it does not transform in accordance with relativity. It is not merely the magnetic field of current theory that does not conform to reality; the electric field does not conform either.

The TEW/vecton theory does transform correctly. Two effects are involved. When an object is moving with velocity v, relativity theory predicts a phenomenon known as "time dilation." The length of time during which any physical process takes place increases by the factor

$$\gamma = \frac{1}{\sqrt{1 - \dfrac{v^2}{c^2}}}.$$

In particular, the time interval between emissions of vectons by a moving charge is increased by this factor. Stated differently, the rate of vecton emission is reduced by the factor

$$\beta = \frac{1}{\gamma} = \sqrt{1 - \frac{v^2}{c^2}},$$

thus reducing the force between the moving electrons by this factor. In addition, relativity theory says that when an object is moving, its mass increases by the factor γ. So the acceleration of the electrons produced by the vectons is reduced by an additional factor of β due to the increased mass. The resulting acceleration of each electron, produced by the vectons from the other electron, is thus reduced by two factors of β, or by a single factor of $\left(1 - \frac{v^2}{c^2}\right)$. This is exactly the correct result.

This does not prove that the vecton theory is correct, merely that it is consistent with relativity, and therefore that it is a viable theory from this point of view. Current electromagnetic theory is not similarly viable.

So, where do the rotated push-vectors come in? Figure 10.6 illustrates the answer. Two electrons are moving side by side. Because they are moving, and because it takes a short period of time for vectons to travel from one electron to the other, a vecton arriving at electron 2 when at the position shown will have been emitted by electron 1 when it was in the earlier position shown by the open dot. The vecton then

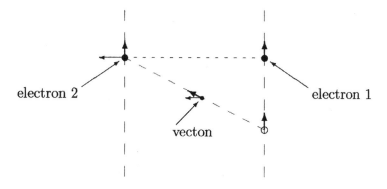

Figure 10.6: Vecton Interaction of Moving Electrons

follows the diagonal path shown. However, due to the Joe Namath effect, the vecton still points in the direction perpendicular to the motion of the electrons. Hence the force between the electrons remains in that perpendicular direction.

The vectons emitted by a charge moving with constant velocity will always point directly away from (or, for negative vectons, directly back toward) the instantaneous position of that charge, not toward the earlier position of the charge when it emitted the vectons.

Figure 10.6 makes clear that the vecton force on a stationary nucleus at the location of electron 2 would not be affected by the motion of electron 1. Because electron 1 is moving, its rate of emission of vectons is reduced by the factor β. However, because the vectons are emitted from the position of electron 1 shown in the figure, electron 1 is getting progressively closer to the position of the stationary nucleus as it emits successive vectons. The distance over which the vectons must travel is thus decreasing for successive vectons, increasing the rate at which vectons arrive at the nucleus by the same factor β. The two effects cancel one another, leading to the unchanged force. In addition, because the nucleus is not moving, there is no increase to its mass. So the vecton picture transforms correctly in this manner also.

In the more general case of currents in wires that are not parallel to one another, the "magnetic" effects result from a complicated combination of relativity and rotatable push-vectors, as do the "electric" effects. All that exists in fact are vectons with "rotating" push-vectors, not separate electric and magnetic "fields." Electromagnetism should be renamed "vecton mechanics."

Vectons are actually photons. Charged particles emit them in response to the elementary waves that are everywhere in free space. TEW, because it separates wave and particle, is able to describe the photons as simple, particulate objects, thereby doing away with the enormously complex photon wave-particles of current quantum mechanical theory. A vecton-like picture of photons is impossible in the context of quantum mechanics. In modern quantum mechanics, a photon cannot be an entity at all, of any kind, by any meaningful definition of "entity." The word "entity" does not appear in the lexicon of many modern physicists. For that matter, neither does the word "reality."

As an aside: if, in the triangle consisting of: 1) the path of the vecton; 2) the motion of electron 1; and 3) the line between the two electrons, the length along the motion of electron 1 is taken as v (the velocity of the electron) and the diagonal line is taken as c, the velocity of the vecton, then, according to the Pythagorean theorem, the line between the two electrons has length

$$\sqrt{(c^2 - v^2)} = c\sqrt{1 - \frac{v^2}{c^2}}.$$

One thus sees, at least in this special case, the origin of the factor $\sqrt{1 - \frac{v^2}{c^2}}$ ubiquitous in relativity theory.

10.5 Faraday's Law

Faraday's law provides the real confirmation that the vecton theory is correct. Physicists have, for more than a century, assumed the correctness of Faraday's law as, in effect, one of the "axioms" of electromagnetic theory. Four equations describing this and three other such "axioms" form the foundation for the entire mathematical/behavioral edifice of current theory. TEW explains all four of these laws, but only the explanation of Faraday's law will be presented here.

As an example of the Faraday effect, consider two simple loops of wire, as illustrated in Figure 10.8. Figure 10.7 shows a side view of the same loops along with the alleged magnetic field generated by a current in the left-hand loop. If an electric current is moving steadily in the left-hand loop, no effect is produced on the right-hand loop, assuming it carries no current. But if the current in the left loop is changed, that change generates a current in the right loop. Varying the current in one loop generates what physicists call an "electromotive force" in the other loop. It is through this effect that electric generators and electric motors operate. The electromotive force in the right loop lasts only as long as the current in the left loop is changing. It is the change to the current in the left loop, not the current itself, that produces the effect.

Current theory says that the current in the left loop produces a magnetic field, as shown in Figure 10.7. A change to the current in the left loop changes the magnitude of the magnetic field. The alleged field still follows similar field lines, but it is stronger or weaker as the

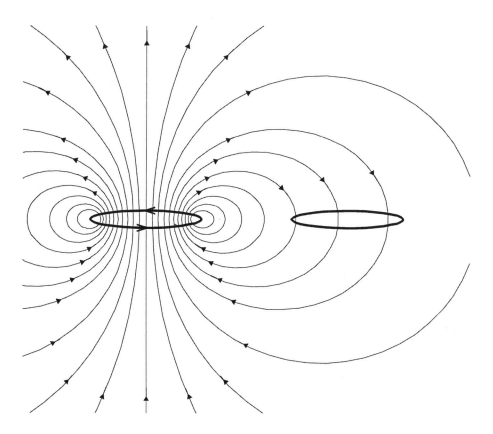

Figure 10.7: Faraday Effect

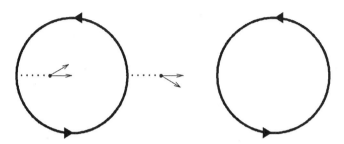

Figure 10.8: Vecton Picture of Faraday Effect

current is increased or decreased. The magnetic field from the left loop passes through the area enclosed by the right loop, as shown in Figure 10.7. A change to the magnetic field penetrating through the right loop is allegedly the cause of the electromotive force in the right loop. The theory does not explain how or why the change to the magnetic field produces the electromotive force, nor do modern physicists even considered this to be explainable. Physicists accept the equation describing the relationship between the changing (alleged) magnetic field and the electromotive force (allegedly) resulting from the changing field simply because it "works"—it accurately predicts the magnitude of the electromotive force.

Right away it is clear why this picture leads to absurdities such as the Aharanov-Bohm effect. It is not merely the change to the magnetic field at the location of the physical wire in the right-hand loop that (allegedly) produces the effect. Changes to the field at locations within the loop, and therefore not in contact with the wire, allegedly contribute. The current picture has a "built-in" nonlocality.

Furthermore, the electromotive force in the right-hand loop doesn't "wait" to form until the increased magnetic field has time to travel around the magnetic field lines and arrive at that loop. Experiment shows that the effect is transmitted on a direct line from one loop to the other, this, again, at the speed of light. Yet anything traveling in a straight line from one loop to the other won't pass through the area of the second loop, at least in the example of Figure 10.7, given that both loops lie in the same plane. The experimental evidence thus contradicts the picture implied by current theory.

Assume for purposes of this illustration that the current in the left loop flows in the direction indicated by the arrows in Figure 10.8. For ease of representation, assume also that the moving particles constituting the current are positively charged, not negatively charged as are the electrons generally making up an electric current. The latter assumption does not change the outcome—the assignment of positive or negative to one charge or the other is arbitrary—but aids in the representation of the effect.

Assuming a current is flowing in the left loop, the figure shows two sample vectons leaving that loop and traveling toward the right loop. The vecton leaving the "near" side—the side closest to the right loop—has its push-vector rotated in the direction indicated. This is the direction in which the vecton would have traveled had the emitting charge been stationary. The vecton leaving the "far" side of the left loop has its push-vector similarly rotated but in the opposite direction. In each case, the vectons shown are balanced by vectons coming from the stationary charges in the wire—the nuclei—whose vectons point in the opposite direction and are not rotated. The product is a downward push due to vectons from the near side, and an upward push due to vectons from the far side.

As vectons from the near side of the left loop arrive at the near side of the right loop—the side closest to the left loop—they produce a push on charges in the right loop in the downward direction in the figure, thereby acting so as to generate a current in the right loop in the counterclockwise direction. But at the same time, similar vectons from the near side of the left loop will be impacting the far side of the right loop and will be pushing with equal force in the clockwise direction. The two forces cancel each other, and no net current is produced in the right loop. Similarly, the vectons from the far side of the left loop will push upward on charges in the near side of the right loop and downward on the far side, also resulting in no net current in the right loop.

Now consider what happens when the current in the left loop is increased. The push-vectors in the vectons emitted by the left loop will be rotated further. This will be true both for the vectons emitted from the near side of the left loop and from the far side. But because the near side is closer to the right loop, the vectons with the increased rotation coming from the near side of the left loop will arrive at the right loop before those from the far side. In addition, those same vectons will arrive at the near side of the right loop before they arrive at the far side.

The net result, for a brief moment, will be an increased push downward on the charges in the wire on the near side of the right loop that is not counterbalanced by any change elsewhere, resulting in a current in the counterclockwise direction in the right loop.

These first vectons to arrive at the right loop will subsequently also impact the far side of the right loop and will push in the opposite, clockwise direction. But as long as the current in the left loop continues to increase, by the time these vectons reach the far side, the rotations of the vectons simultaneously arriving at the near side will have increased still further. The result is a steady counterclockwise push to the current in the right loop.

Vectons from the far side of the left loop also arrive, and, by the same reasoning, act so as to produce a current in the right loop in the clockwise direction. But because the far side of the left loop is further away from the right loop, the effect is smaller than that produced by the near side vectons. Due to their three-dimensional radial motion away from the emitting charges, the vectons from the far side will have spread apart from each other more than those from the near side, so fewer will impact the wires of the right loop. The overall result of the vectons from both sides of the left loop is thus a current in the right loop in the counterclockwise direction.

If one assigns values to the parameters describing the vectons so as to satisfy Coulomb's law describing the interaction of two stationary charges, this picture of the Faraday effect exactly reproduces the quantitative predictions of current theory in every detail. This remains true for any relative orientation of the two loops as well as for any size and shape of each loop. This picture actually explains the Faraday effect, as opposed to merely assuming it because the formulas work.

One detail in particular warrants mention: Faraday's law says that the magnitude of the Faraday effect is proportional to $1/c^2$, where c, again, is the velocity of light. In current theory, this dependence on the velocity of light receives no physical explanation. Indeed, in one system of units that physicists employ, the formula describing the Faraday effect has it proportional to $1/c$, not $1/c^2$. In the vecton picture, the time it takes for vectons to travel from the far side of the left loop to the near side—the time by which the far side vectons lag those from the near side—is proportional to $1/c$. A faster velocity of light would mean a shorter time lag, and thus a smaller Faraday effect. Similarly, the time it takes for vectons to travel across the right loop is also proportional to $1/c$. Hence the dependence of the overall effect on $1/c^2$. Each factor of $1/c$ represents a physical aspect of the overall Faraday effect. These effects are not apparent in current theory.

The vecton explanation involves no nonlocality. Each vecton affects a charged particle only upon making actual contact with it.

The picture implied by current theory completely misstates the time and location of the individual physical events that give rise to the Faraday effect. This is true for magnetic phenomena in general. This is why physicists incorrectly interpret the Aharanov-Bohm effect as implying, in effect, a nonlocal interaction between the "magnetic field" at one location and the effect on particles at another location. In fact, at the location of the affected particles, vectons are present and produce the observed effect.

Observe still one more time the somersault philosophy: Physicists rationalize the contradictions emerging from the magnetic field picture by maintaining that the only test of a "theory" is whether or not it "works"—that they are only developing a formalism, not a physical picture of things. The magnetic field picture "works"—it, along with quantum mechanics, correctly predicts the Aharanov-Bohm effect. So if modern physicists really did view the magnetic field "picture" as merely a formalism that works, why did they consider the Aharanov-Bohm effect to be noteworthy in the first place? Only if they viewed the magnetic field picture as an actual picture of reality would they consider the "nonlocality" of Aharanov-Bohm to be problematical.

In their efforts to understand magnetism, as with so many other phenomena, physicists are boxed in by their formalism. That formalism dictates that interactions between particles must conserve momentum and that the momentum of a moving particle points along the direction of the particle's motion. The notion of a rotated push-vector is thus "out of bounds." If physicists actually did view momentum conservation merely as a formalism that "works" in describing the interactions of some objects, why would they conclude that the same description would necessarily apply to all interactions? Clearly, once again, they are treating their behavioral formalism as if it constituted reality—as if the momentum resulting from an object's motion were the cause of the object's effect on other objects.

10.6 Electromagnetic Waves

Chapter 9 explained that one obtains the laws of classical physics in the limit of very short wavelengths of the elementary waves, making it possible to ignore the waves and describe the behaviors of objects as if they interacted directly with other objects rather than through the intermediation of elementary waves. Presumably this relationship would apply to the laws of classical electricity and magnetism as well. But what about radio waves, radar, and other "classical" waves of everyday experience?

The rotated push-vector theory directly provides the explanation. Figure 10.9 depicts a row of vectons traveling to the right along a single line. The additional vectors attached to each vecton are the push-vectors. The oscillating charge on the left of the figure has emitted the vectons. The first vecton on the far right was emitted when the oscillating charge was stationary at the highest point of its oscillation. The next vecton was emitted as the charge started to move down. The third vecton was emitted when the charge was moving down with its greatest velocity. The charge then slowed down and emitted the fourth vecton, then stopped and emitted the fifth vecton. The charge then moved up and emitted the next vectons according to the same description, except that now the push-vectors are rotated down instead of up.

As this row of vectons impacts an absorbing charge, successive vectons will cause the charge to move up and down. Assume again that electrons are positive and protons negative, and that the oscillating charge on the left in the figure is an electron in an antenna. A row of negative vectons coming from the nuclei of the atoms in the antenna

Figure 10.9: Vecton Waves

would balance the vectons in the figure coming from the electron. Because the nuclei do not oscillate, the latter vecton's push-vectors would not be rotated. The effect of the sum of these two rows of vectons would be to cause an absorbing electron to oscillate in a straight up and down direction.

The net result is that the oscillating charge in an antenna on the left sends out a "wave" made up of the vectons. An electron in a receiving antenna somewhere to the right of the figure absorbs the wave, causing the electron to oscillate. This is the actual physical picture of the transmission of classical radio waves, radar waves, and the like. Notice that these "waves" travel in the same direction as the particles—the vectons—as they must since they are composed of those vectons.

Figure 10.9 shows only a few typical vectons. A real wave will have many vectons in the spaces between those shown in the figure, with their push vectors changing more gradually. The individual vectons are too small for their individual effects to be noticeable. The effect on an absorbing charge is that of a smoothly varying wave.

The elementary waves involved in the process depicted in Figure 10.9 are not shown in the figure. They are traveling to the left, toward the oscillating charge, coming, for example, from the electron in the receiving antenna mentioned above. They impact the oscillating electron on the left and stimulate the emission of vectons shown in the figure.

Consider the overall wave picture when, say, a radar detector is used to measure the speed of a car. First, elementary waves are present moving from the car to the radar machine. Those elementary waves stimulate the emission of the particle vectons that make up the radar wave that travels from the radar machine to the car. Those vectons cause electrons in the metal of the car to oscillate. Those oscillating electrons in turn emit vectons in response to elementary waves coming from the radar machine. Those vectons then constitute the radar wave that returns to the radar machine, producing oscillations, which the machine measures. Hence the speeding ticket.

Current theory describes electromagnetic waves as a self-regenerating combination of electric and magnetic "fields." Changing electric fields generate magnetic fields, which in turn generate electric fields, etc. Figure 10.10 shows such a wave. The solid line represents the electric field, the dashed line the magnetic. The physicist James Clerk Maxwell

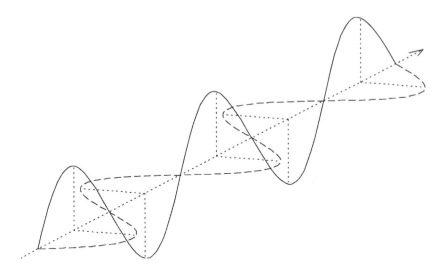

Figure 10.10: Maxwell Wave

discovered that such a wave combination is self-sustaining—it will propagate over long distances while retaining this same form.

Behaviorally speaking, the vecton picture is identical. For the special case of these waves, the push-vectors of the vectons do correspond to the electric field of current theory. An imaginary vector perpendicular to both the push-vector and the velocity vector of each vecton then corresponds to the magnetic field. If **E** represents the push vector and **c** the velocity of the vecton, the imaginary magnetic vector **B** would be given by

$$\mathbf{B} = \frac{1}{c}\mathbf{c} \times \mathbf{v},$$

where the × represents the usual cross-product of vector mathematics. Referring to the right-hand half of Figure 10.4, an imaginary magnetic vector attached to the vectons in the top half of the figure would point downward into the paper. The imaginary magnetic vector for the vectons on the bottom would point upward out of the paper. If one imagines attaching the magnetic vector to each vecton in the row in Figure 10.9, the result would look exactly like Figure 10.10. Dynamically speaking, however, all that is happening in fact is that vectons are moving along the long dotted line carrying their rotated push-vectors. The Maxwell theory involves an enormously complicated dynamics for the switching back and forth of the electric and magnetic fields, all of which is totally fictitious. And, true to the somersault philosophy, physicists treat the dynamics as if it describes what actually occurs in reality.

Because quantum mechanics has the quantum waves moving in the same direction as the particle photons, and because the mathematics of the photon quantum waves is the same as that of the vecton waves, quantum mechanics ends up treating the two waves as if they were one and the same object. In fact, the two waves not only move in opposite directions, they are totally different in kind.

Current electrodynamic theory illustrates the fact that the unreal formalism of modern physics began to build up even prior to the formulation of quantum mechanics. Maxwell left out reality. He assumed, in effect, if not by intention, that "electric" and "magnetic" behaviors could be produced, not by real entities, but by nothing.

Chapter 11

MODERN PHYSICS

11.1 Modern Physics

Modern physics might best be described as a giant edifice of interlocking mathematical formulas describing behavior—not behavior of anything, just behavior. This edifice rests on a foundation consisting primarily of Newtonian mechanics and Maxwellian electromagnetism. Chapter 10 documented the fact that at least the latter of these two theories incorporates fictitious electric and magnetic fields, composed of "their" behavior, along with a fictitious dynamics of those fictitious fields. The basic concept of mass in Newtonian mechanics is defined— if modern physicists choose to define it at all—solely in terms of the behavior "it" produces.

The behavioral effects described by these classical theories are certainly real, and they do occur as described by the relevant equations. But physicists lost sight of the fact that behavior is always behavior of something. Instead of seeking knowledge of the real entities producing the behavior, they took behavior as being, in effect, the primary existent. They viewed real objects as being composed of their behavior. In the case of the magnetic field, they made behavior into an object that doesn't exist at all. Classical physicists, nonetheless, still had enough connection to reality to view these various objects, at least implicitly, as being real—as allegedly being the way things are in reality.

Then came quantum mechanics. Physicists observed the wavelike behavior of particles. So they added to their formalism equations describing a fictitious wave coming from the particle source. That's what the behavior looked like, so this must be the way things are in reality.

Sure enough, follow the formulas and you obtain the pattern observed "on the screen." Except that now this allegedly existing wave isn't really real. It's merely a formula that "works." And the behavior itself isn't actual behavior, it is merely the probability that actual behavior will occur. Contradictions become okay. The mathematical formalism acquires a life of its own. It becomes the new reality.

As the 20th century unfolded, the formalism continued to grow. No longer restrained by the requirements of logical consistency— consistency, that is, with reality—by mid-century the formalism had run totally out of control. Physicists came to be utterly lost in this new, formulaic reality. It was as if physicists had discovered the ideal world of Plato's "forms," except that Plato had been mistaken: They weren't "forms," they were "fields." Theories began to appear that were either totally vacuous or had so little connection to any real objects as to be effectively vacuous. One such "theory" is known today as the theory of the "violation of parity."

11.2 Parity Violation

In 1957, physicists performed an experiment demonstrating that when subatomic particles interact with one another through what is known as the "weak" interactions, they act in a non-symmetrical or handed manner. Figure 11.1a illustrates a process that can occur when a particle known as a π^- meson collides with a proton p. The interaction transforms the two particles into two different particles: a Λ^0 particle and a K^0 meson. The Λ^0 then subsequently decays back into a proton and a π^- meson. The figure is a two-dimensional representation of a three-dimensional process; the initial π^- and the two dashed lines showing the paths of the Λ^0 and K^0 lie in the same horizontal plane; the final proton goes up relative to that plane, the final π^- down. We can see that this decay pattern is handed by comparing it with Figure 11.1b, its mirror image. In Figure 11.1a, imagine placing your left arm along the path of the initial π^- with your left hand held in a position such that the direction of the curl of your fingers would sweep the path of the K^0 into that of the Λ^0. Your thumb ends up pointing in the direction of the path of the final p. In order to accomplish the same thing with Figure 11.1b, you must use your right hand.

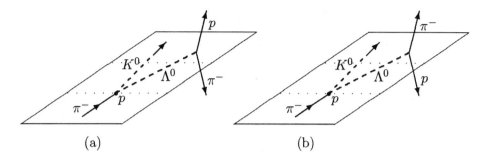

(a)   (b)

Figure 11.1: Lambda Decay

When a π^- interacts with a proton, both of these decay patterns can occur, but 11.1b occurs less frequently than 11.1a. The two decay processes are not "on a par" with each other—there is a lack of "parity" between the right-handed and the left-handed process. The decay process "violates parity."

In 1956, when physicists T. D. Lee and C. N. Yang first proposed that the "weak interactions" between particles might not "conserve parity," this idea was revolutionary. The "strong" and "electromagnetic" interactions of particles had been found to "conserve parity", and the then-current, giant mathematical formalism describing particle behavior reflected this fact. With the experimental confirmation that the weak interactions violate parity, significant additions to that formalism became necessary. With the inclusion of parity violation, it became possible to tie the mathematical description of the weak interactions in with the formalism describing the other interactions.

But the significance of this "theory" was solely formulaic. It merely required a change to the formalism. In fact, the "theory" explains exactly nothing. True, the fact that the weak interactions involve handedness helped to explain why the formalism hadn't been able to "work" previously in describing the results of the weak interactions. So the fact of handed behavior did explain something. But to the question, "Why does the handed behavior occur?" the theory says nothing. To say that the handed behavior occurs because parity is violated is not a theory; it is a redundancy.

Parity violation is an anti-theory. It says, in effect, that the handed behavior just happens—for no reason. If one thinks in terms of real objects and not formalism, there is no other manner in which to interpret the "theory." As such, the parity-violation theory has served to squelch any attempt to discover the actual reason for the handed behavior.

The theory of parity violation was awarded a Nobel Prize in 1957.

11.3 Theoretical Significance of the Handed Behavior

The reason for the handed behavior is virtually self-evident, and recognition of the reason leads to a number of useful identifications.

First of all, if an object behaves in a handed manner, clearly that object itself must be handed. If an object were symmetrical—if the object were the same as its mirror image—then its behavior would have to be symmetrical. If the behavior of a symmetrical object could be asymmetrical, then a mirror image of the object together with its behavior would mean that the same object—itself and its identical mirror image—could produce different behaviors. The differences in behavior would thus result from nothing, which is absurd. Nothing can't do anything. Only an asymmetrical object can produce asymmetrical behavior. Subatomic particles exhibiting handed behavior are necessarily handed objects. (Even if a handedness of the elementary wave that a particle follows is responsible for the handed behavior, the particle itself would have to be handed in order to explain why it follows that elementary wave and not the wave's mirror image.)

Experiments have shown, furthermore, that for all subatomic particles, with the exception of K^0 mesons, whatever handed behavior a particle displays, its so-called "anti-particle" exhibits behavior that is the exact mirror image. The probability of any behaviors of any system of particles that does not include K^0 mesons is always equal to the probability of the mirror-image behaviors of the same system of anti-particles. The K^0 meson exhibits the exceptional behavior perhaps because it is a "composite" particle that simultaneously follows two elementary waves of differing wavelength.

Again there is an obvious conclusion: Anti-particles are in fact nothing more than the mirror image of particles. If all behaviors of one are the mirror image of all behaviors of the other, were the particles and anti-particles not themselves mirror images of one another, some of the mirror-image behavior of one or the other would be coming from nothing, by an argument similar to the one just put forward for a symmetrical object. Only if there were some as-yet-undiscovered behaviors that were not mirror images of one another could the particles not be mirror images.

Modern physicists even have a law for this relationship between particle and anti-particle, called the CP theorem. P stands for taking the mirror image, and C stands for changing particle into anti-particle. All particle behaviors, other than those of the K^0, are "invariant under CP." And yet, even with this law, modern physicists have not drawn the obvious conclusion. They are so caught up with the formalism into which the CP theorem fits that they have lost altogether the ability to think in terms of the real objects involved. Indeed, the formalism of quantum mechanics militates against a picture in which particles have an inner structure, as discussed in Section 5.4.

Numerous additional conclusions follow from the above facts. A π^0 meson, for example, is known to be its own anti-particle—the two are the same particle. Conclusion: because the mirror image of the π^0 is that same particle, the π^0 meson must be symmetrical. It is by putting two and two together in this manner that one determines, from the observed behaviors, what the objects themselves look like. But this methodology requires recognition of the fact that one is always dealing with real objects, not disembodied, uncaused behavior.

11.4 "Dark Matter"

Perhaps the most preposterous example of physicists putting formalism above reality is the current "kick" among theoreticians known as "dark matter."

The "leading lights" among modern physicists, at least in the United States, have proclaimed that gravity is the primary force determining the structure of the universe on a cosmological scale. Einstein's "general theory of relativity," which integrates gravity with the "special theory of relativity" described in Chapter 7, is supposedly the end-all theory of cosmology.

In studying the behavior of galaxies, however, physicists discovered that the quantity of mass within galaxies is insufficient to produce the gravitational force necessary to hold together the stars making up those galaxies. Galaxies are spinning collections of stars. The stars must attract one another or the centrifugal force due to the spinning of the galaxy would cause them to fly apart from one another. Given the rate at which most galaxies are spinning, there simply isn't enough mass to produce the necessary gravitational force.

But the theory is sacrosanct. Modern physicists decided that there must be more mass present than what they had observed. Indeed, they claim that the total mass actually present is ten times greater than the mass of what is visible, with ninety percent of the total mass being "dark"—that is, invisible. They "save" the theory by claiming that ninety percent of the universe is invisible!

This "reasoning" is so absurd it barely deserves comment. True, if one sees, for example, an unexplained force on a planet, perhaps indicating the existence of another, as-yet-undiscovered planet, it would be reasonable to look for the as-yet-undiscovered planet. But to invent literally nine times the total of all known objects in the universe…? "Dark matter" should properly be termed "ghost matter." Modern physicists have spent many tens of millions of taxpayer dollars chasing this ghost.

What makes ghost matter even more preposterous is the fact that a mere glance at the universe confirms overwhelmingly that something other than gravity must play a significant role. Gravity is a "central force;" it pulls identically from all directions, inward toward the center of any massive body. So if gravity were the only significant force, one would expect to find primarily spherically symmetrical collections of stars or other objects held together by that gravity. And yet, of all the objects astronomers have seen, only a tiny fraction are of this form. The stars in galaxies almost invariably circle more or less in a single plane. The orbits of the planets in our solar system all lie in a single plane, with the exception of (now non-planet) Pluto, the plane of whose orbit is slightly tipped relative to the other planets. Saturn's rings lie very precisely in a single plane. And so on. All of this evidence cries out for what physicists term a "cross-product" force. Electromagnetism is a cross-product force—the only known long range, cross-product force. Yet modern theoretical physicists are so adamant that gravity must explain everything that any physicist who suggests otherwise (at least in the United States) could thereby literally end his academic career.

Meanwhile, a physicist in Sweden by the name of Hannes Alfvén has explained the missing force as being electromagnetic and, based on his theory, has made predictions of previously unknown phenomena that astronomers have since confirmed. This work by Alfvén has been largely ignored in the United States, this in spite of the fact that Alfvén was awarded a Nobel Prize—and a deserved one at that—for some of his earlier work.

Modern physicists claim that they have observed a number of instances of "gravitational lensing." Light from a far distant object—presumably a galaxy—is allegedly bent in the gravitational field of a massive body lying between the earth and the distant object. But in order to produce the degree of alleged bending that is allegedly observed, the mass of the object producing the bending would have to be many times larger than the mass of any visible object. Modern physicists claim here again that the "missing" mass is unseen, "dark" matter.

Sound experiments show that gravity does cause light rays to bend. Massive bodies can, in principle, cause a lensing effect. Gravitational lensing, however, could not possibly cause the patterns of light actually observed in many, if not all, of the examples of alleged lensing. In many instances, what a photograph reveals is a short, curved line, or arc, of light. The line generally is of uniform width and brightness. But if lensing were the cause of the arc, the line would be wider, or at least brighter, toward the middle of the arc and narrower, or dimmer, toward the ends.[1] This is not the case for many of the alleged instances of lensing. For many of the arcs that have been recorded, the photograph shows clear evidence that what is actually being observed is a shock wave of matter resulting from an explosion of some sort in the distant past.

Physicists have observed no instance of alleged lensing that can reasonably be interpreted as providing evidence for invisible, "dark" matter. Instead, they have started with the result they want—the dark matter—and "twisted" the photographic evidence to fit their theory. The editors of American physics journals have frequently been guilty of what can only be described as suppression of evidence when that

---

[1] See, for example, Halton Arp, *Seeing Red*, Apeiron, Quebec (1998), p. 169ff.

evidence conflicted with the notions of dark matter, "the big bang" and other modern cosmological theories.[2]

11.5 Humian Behaviorism versus Reality

The British philosopher David Hume, in his influential *An Enquiry Concerning Human Understanding*, argued against the validity of the principle of cause and effect. Hume's argument, in essence, was the following: When one billiard ball runs into another and the second ball then moves, I see one motion, then I see the second motion, and I see that the two motions are related to one another, but nowhere do I see any "cause." Because I (allegedly) observe nothing beyond the motions and their relationship, any notion of causation lacks empirical verification and therefore lies outside the realm of science.

Hume was writing in the context of the "Aristotelian" view of physics (which, in fact, was blatantly non-Aristotelian) that preceded the scientific Enlightenment. In that view, the actions of physical entities were caused by mystical inner "essences" of the entities, or were deduced from allegedly self-evident principles, principles that were in fact completely arbitrary. These "essences" and "principles" generally lacked any basis in observed fact. Entities acted as they did because of their "nature," with the latter being understood as consisting of such mystical "essences" or the like.

Hume was, of course, correct in rejecting such overt rationalism. His response, however, was equally non-empirical. Hume didn't see two motions and their relationship. What Hume saw was two moving *billiard balls*.

Behavior is, and can only be, behavior *of something*. Hume didn't see nothing moving, he saw billiard balls moving. Walking cannot exist without the being who walks, Bertrand Russell notwithstanding. Any action presupposes an actor. "Action of nothing" is a contradiction in terms.

In response to Hume's claim that he saw no cause, it would be tempting to say, in a loud tone of voice: "The cause was the billiard ball, stupid!" Why did the first billiard ball affect the second as it did? Because

---

[2] Ibid.

a billiard ball is made up of a relatively solid but nonetheless somewhat elastic material, is heavy enough to impart a certain momentum to the second billiard ball, etc. Why did the second billiard ball respond as it did? For the same reasons. The billiard balls acted as they did because of what they are. Consider what the response of the second ball would have been had it instead been a rotten tomato. Clearly the response would have been quite different, because a rotten tomato is a different kind of entity.

Entities act as they do because they are what they are. This is the law of cause and effect. Causality is not a motion-motion relationship, as Hume conceived it. It is an entity-action relationship. Hume forgot the entities, and physicists have continued to forget them ever since.

One explains why something acts as it does by discovering what it is—by discovering its real nature.

Frequently we learn what something is by first observing its behavior. We then put two and two together to make a hypothesis as to what it might consist of. We then test that hypothesis against all available evidence. Many examples of this process have been presented in this volume. In all of them there was the guiding principle that when something happens, something—something real—did it. And being real, it can only be what it is, not what it isn't. Accepting contradictions negates the entire method; indeed, it negates as purposeless any effort to try to learn anything.

So, physicists observe the wavelike pattern on the screen in the double-slit experiment. It certainly appears as if a wave is coming from the particle source. Physicists formulate a hypothesis to that effect. But they then find that with that hypothesis they cannot account for the behavior of the individual particles. The hypothesis fails. The present author then proposes the reciprocal-wave picture of TEW. This hypothesis accounts for all the evidence, without contradiction. In addition, it predicts relativity. Therefore, it must be the way things actually are in reality.

Physicists observe the pushes and pulls of a magnet. It appears as if there is something moving through space in the direction of those pushes and pulls. Physicists hypothesize the magnetic field—that is, a "field" of real stuff of some kind looking like what has been termed the magnetic field. Physicists then come across the Faraday effect, demonstrating that if the field picture were correct it would require action at a distance between the field and a wire in which an electromotive force is induced. One must then scrap that hypothesis and seek another. And so on.

The fact that we begin the process by observing behavioral effects of some kind does not mean that we must stop there. Going further and exploring the causes of these effects does not necessitate the acceptance of anything not grounded on sound empirical evidence. Two basic principles, both validated by vast quantities of empirical evidence, must guide this further quest: 1) If something happens, something caused it—something real. 2) Whatever is real can only be what it is, not what it isn't; contradictions don't exist in reality; A is A.

No mystical "essences" of objects are involved in this methodology. In fact, it is the behavioral philosophy that leads to the embrace of mystical objects—objects such as the forward wave and the magnetic field.

11.6 Grand Unification

Modern theoreticians represent "grand unification" as the holy grail of physics—the ultimate theory of everything. In fact, it would represent the ultimate anti-theory of everything.

The goal of the grand unifiers is to come up with one giant, "unified" formalism describing, not the real universe we see, but a mythical universe consisting solely of disembodied behavior. They want to complete the job of reducing everything in the universe to mathematical equations describing "fields."

Modern physicists go to great lengths to tout their empiricist credentials. Yet, when I open my eyes, I see a computer screen, a desk, books, a window...I see *entities*. Nowhere do I see a field-equation.

Chapter 12

PHYSICS OF THE ATOM

12.1 Wave Structure of the Atom

It was through their investigation of atoms that physicists uncovered much of the early evidence that the laws of classical physics could not account for phenomena at the subatomic level. According to classical physics, for example, an electron orbiting an atomic nucleus should continually emit electromagnetic radiation, thereby gradually losing energy. The energy loss should stop only when the electron loses enough energy to spiral down and collide with the nucleus. Physicists observed, however, that the circling electrons actually lose energy in discrete jumps, or "quanta" (hence "quantum mechanics"), between which they emit no radiation. There is also a lowest energy, or "ground" state, of the electron, in which the electron emits no further radiation, remaining indefinitely in that state unless disturbed.

Niels Bohr created an early model of the hydrogen atom—containing a single circling electron—in which the electron was restricted to a number of discrete "energy levels," with energy specified by a particular mathematical formula, emitting radiation only upon jumping between those levels. While this model made predictions that were approximately correct, it was only after physicists recognized that waves govern the behaviors of the electrons that they were able to develop a formalism that made accurate predictions of the energy of the various levels and other behaviors of the atom.

According to quantum mechanics, an electron in an atom can have a particular energy only if, in effect, its wave "fits" at that level. As the wave propagates multiple times around the nucleus, the wave must be self-reinforcing, much as is the case for the waves in a resonant cavity described in Section 2.4. The situation in the atom, however, is more complicated than that for the resonant cavity. The wave in the atom doesn't propagate along merely a simple circle around the nucleus, analogous to the straight back-and-forth propagation in the resonant cavity. The wave, instead, fills the entire volume around the nucleus.

The two situations are nonetheless analogous with respect to the problem they pose for quantum mechanics—the same problem identified in Section 2.4 for the resonant cavity. When an electron jumps from a higher to a lower level, somehow the lower level has to affect the electron in the higher level in order to cause the electron to jump specifically to that lower level. But until the electron "wave-particle" has already jumped to the lower level, there is nothing in the lower level, and therefore nothing to cause the jump. A "level," absent any wave in that level, is nothing. It is merely another "available state." Speaking figuratively, if the only wave involved is that of the electron "wave-particle," how does the electron "know" ahead of time where to jump—where its wave will "fit?"

According to quantum mechanics, the various "available states" constituting the energy levels are in continual interaction with one another; the available states aren't real things, but they nonetheless interact! Quantum mechanics does make accurate predictions of the energies of the various levels; but, as with the resonant cavity experiments, the postulated physical picture makes no sense. The picture makes sense only if a real wave already exists at every level to which an electron might jump. This is precisely the TEW picture. The available states are made up of real elementary waves.

In the vicinity of an atomic nucleus, photon waves that have interacted with the nucleus will in turn interact with electron waves already present in the environment. The electron waves coming from different directions are connected to one another, as described in Section 7.5, upon interaction with the photon waves. The result is the formation of electron wave orbitals around the nucleus. Although composed of many interconnected elementary wave pieces, an orbital will affect an electron particle as if it were a single wave orbiting the nucleus.

Orbitals of all wave frequency are present around the nucleus at all times. However, only the orbitals that fit will affect an electron particle.

These are the orbitals that, by virtue of their particular wavelength, reinforce themselves upon multiple trips around the nucleus, just as with the waves that fit in the resonant cavity. Orbitals that don't fit will self-cancel their potential effect on an electron upon making the multiple trips. According to TEW, a particle electron will end up following a wave only if it is stimulated to do so by that wave. Only the orbitals that fit will have sufficient net amplitude to produce such stimulation. Hence electrons will end up following only these wave orbitals.

A single energy level in an atom is actually composed of a multitude of orbitals. Most of the orbitals making up an energy level are not simple circles around the nucleus; orbitals come in many sizes and shapes. The total wave object for each energy level in an atom is the product of the constructive interference of this multitude of differing wave orbitals.

12.2 How an Electron Follows Its Wave

The mechanics by which an electron follows its wave in an atom is the same mechanics by which all particles follow their waves. Elementary waves do not steer particles by exerting pushes or pulls on them. When a wave has been deflected, a particle following the wave (in reverse) will deflect along the initial path of its wave while simultaneously emitting or absorbing another, "secondary" particle. The same elementary wave that caused the deflection of the particle's wave to begin with stimulates the emission or absorption of the secondary particle.

Consider an example: An electron elementary wave flux is first traveling along a line in a particular direction, and a photon wave flux intersecting it deflects it into a new direction, as shown in Figure 12.1. A deflection of the wave, as described in Section 7.5, does not mean that the same physical wave has changed course but instead means that the initial wave connects with a different, already present wave traveling in the new direction. The connection passes the marker and phase of the first wave onto the second. Along comes a particle electron following the second wave—in reverse as usual. When the electron arrives at the point where the electron wave was deflected, the photon wave that caused that deflection stimulates the emission of a particle photon from the electron. Simultaneously, the initial electron wave stimulates the electron to follow it. The electron responds to that particular wave

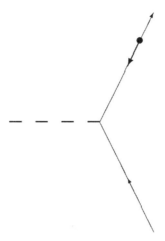

Figure 12.1: Particle follows wave

instead of other electron waves in the vicinity because that wave carries the marker that the electron is following.

The deflection of the electron while emitting the photon might be described as conserving momentum. The momentum of the photon will in fact be equal and opposite to the change in the momentum of the electron. But it is not any principle of conservation of momentum that causes the process to occur in this manner. It is the manner in which the waves interacted to begin with that causes the particles to act so as to conserve momentum. The electron deflects as it does because its new direction is the direction from which its wave is coming. The wavelength of the photon wave that initially caused the electron wave to deflect determines the momentum of the photon.

This same mechanism causes the electron, after its deflection, to continue following its wave. As long as the wave doesn't deflect, the electron simply continues moving in the same direction. The wave has no effect on the particle as long as the wave isn't deflected. When the wave is again deflected in another interaction with another photon wave, the process repeats itself.

Not just any photon wave can bring about the process shown in Figure 12.1. This process won't occur in free space, away from other particles. The photon wave required would necessarily have originated at another charged particle nearby, such as the nucleus in the atom.

This is the process by which an electron follows its wave in the atom.

12.3 Atomic Decay

Atomic decay is the process in which an electron in an atom jumps from a higher energy level to a lower energy level and simultaneously emits a photon.

Figure 12.2 illustrates one manner in which this might occur. The electron wave in the lower energy level first interacts with a photon wave coming from the nucleus and then immediately interacts with a photon wave coming from outside the atom, thereby connecting the electron wave in the lower level to the electron wave in the upper level. Photon waves are present throughout space in the vicinity of the atom. The wave coming from outside the atom is one of those waves. An electron following the upper level wave might then arrive at the point of the interaction with the outside photon wave. The photon wave stimulates the emission of a photon by the electron, with the photon then traveling off into space. The wave from the nucleus then immediately stimulates emission of a second photon that travels to the nucleus. The electron then continues to follow the wave in the lower energy level.

The extent to which the waves in the upper and lower levels interact through processes such as that in Figure 12.2 determines the probability that this decay takes place. The greater the interaction, the higher the probability that an electron in the upper level will end up following the

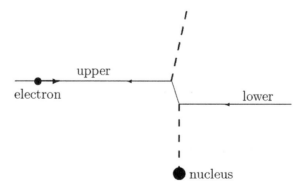

Figure 12.2: Atomic Decay

specific orbital in that level that interacts with the photon waves in the manner illustrated.

The interaction between the two levels occurs throughout the volume of the atom, not merely at the one point where the process of Figure 12.2 takes place. This is why the supporters of quantum mechanics maintain that it is impossible to picture the decay in any manner similar to Figure 12.2. In quantum mechanics, the particle and the wave are one. Given that the probability of the decay results from an interaction between the waves (the "available states") throughout the atom, quantum mechanics is forced to conclude that the electron is located everywhere throughout the atom and that the decay takes place throughout the atom, not at any one location in particular. This picture, furthermore, forces physicists to conclude that the waves and their interactions determine at most the *probability* that a decay will occur. Whether the decay occurs at one time or another is solely a matter of chance. The decay itself is caused by…nothing.

According to TEW, the interaction between the elementary waves occurs throughout the atom, but the decay takes place at a single location: the point where the external photon wave interacted with the specific orbital that the electron follows. An experimenter will not know in advance which specific orbital in a level the electron will follow or where the interaction with the external photon wave occurs. But this is solely a lack of knowledge on the part of the experimenter. The physical process itself is strictly causal and deterministic. Nothing occurs by chance.

The orbitals making up an energy level do not all have precisely identical frequencies. Instead, a level contains orbitals with a small range of frequencies around some central value. Just as the interferometer in the Kaiser experiment discussed in Chapters 3 and 5 would pass waves with a frequency that differs slightly from the central value, orbitals with a frequency close to but not identical with the central frequency of a level will still self-reinforce at least to some degree upon multiple "trips" around the nucleus. Quantum mechanics, as related in Chapter 5 for the Kaiser experiment, is forced to conclude that the energy of an electron in a level is "uncertain"—that it has no one energy in particular. The change in energy of an electron when it jumps between levels is thus also uncertain, as is the energy of the photon emitted from the atom.

According to TEW, also as related in Chapter 5, the elementary wave orbitals in a level have a range of frequencies, but the electron follows only one of them. In atomic decay, an electron jumps between orbitals in each level having one exact frequency. The size of this one energy jump thus has exactly one value, and the emitted photon has exactly one energy. Different orbitals in each level have different frequencies and an electron might follow any one of them. If an atom is excited multiple times so that it decays multiple times between the same two levels, the size of the jump and therefore the energy of the emitted photon will differ slightly from decay to decay. But TEW explains this variation rather than attributing it to some meaningless uncertainty principle.

Quantum mechanics maintains that atomic decay occurs by chance at no location in particular between levels of "uncertain" energy. TEW demonstrates that atomic decay in fact occurs in a strictly causal, deterministic manner at a single location between orbitals of exact frequency.

The quantum mechanical wave function for an atomic level becomes less and less intense as one moves away from the atom, but the mathematics shows that some very small intensity persists even at long distances. Because in quantum mechanics the wave is the particle, modern physicists frequently make statements to the effect that an electron in an atom in New York City has at least some probability of simultaneously being in Chicago!

12.4 Pauli Exclusion Principle

As an electron follows the wave in a particular energy level in an atom, it interacts with other electron waves in its vicinity. One result of that interaction is to bring about a duplicate of the wave the electron is following, except that the duplicate is exactly out of phase with the initial wave. The electron still follows the initial wave; the electron carries the marker of that wave and thus will respond to it in spite of the presence of the second wave. If a second electron comes along, however, it will not see any wave in the level; the out-of-phase duplicate exactly cancels out any possible stimulative effect of the initial wave on the second electron. There is thus no stimulation for the second electron to join that level.

As a result, only one electron will occupy a single level at a time. This explains the Pauli exclusion principle.

Particles that physicists term "bosons" similarly bring about a duplicate wave, but the duplicate is in phase with the original. The duplicate thus enhances the initial wave, providing increased stimulus for additional particles to join the state. The stimulus increases still further with each additional particle, leading, among other phenomena, to what physicists term "Bose-Einstein condensation."

Quantum mechanics is unable to account for the Pauli principle in this simple manner because it cannot separate the wave and the particle. Instead, physicists have invented an enormously complicated mathematical formalism designed to capture this effect solely with the waves. The behavioral objects created in this formalism are utterly unphysical. For example, when one rotates the quantum mechanical wave-function of an electron by 360 degrees, one ends up not with the same wave-function but with its negative, clearly a physically impossible result for any real object.

Chapter 13

THE FUTURE

13.1 Possible Application to Biology/Neurology

Chapter 8 described the "diffraction" of subatomic particles by single-crystals. The TEW explanation demonstrated that the scattering of elementary waves throughout a large volume of the single-crystal affects a "diffracting" particle, even though the particle is sharply localized at all times during the process. In a real sense, the overall structure of the crystal affects the particle's motion.

While the interaction of subatomic particles with single-crystals is admittedly a somewhat singular phenomenon, it illustrates an aspect of TEW that might have significant application to biology and especially to neurobiology. In the right circumstances, the structure of a large scale, macroscopic body can directly affect the motion of individual electrons or other particles. Instead of a situation in which each electron or ion in the body is directly affected only by the atoms, molecules or electrons in its immediate vicinity, perhaps the elementary waves guiding a particle's motion reflect the entire structure of the body or of some macroscopic portion of the body. Perhaps this aspect of TEW, and not merely the existence of fast-moving electrical signals, explains why the brain functions—or appears to function—as a unit when one is conscious and thinking. Perhaps the presence of an organized system of elementary waves in the body constitutes an essential aspect of being alive, in which case the disruption of that system might be the ultimate cause of death for any living being, perhaps including even plants.

The elementary waves might also play a role in the functioning of genetic molecules, whereby the molecule as a whole produces effects on its environment. This might also be the case in the interactions of smaller molecules.

It might even be the case that the appearance of organized elementary waves within organic molecules began the entire process of evolution resulting in living species—species that are living specifically because their systems rely upon organized elementary waves.

While highly speculative, the general suggestion here is that elementary waves, as real objects in their own right, might provide the "missing link" to the next higher level in our understanding of the human and other biological systems and even of molecular chemistry.

13.2 Conservation of Momentum and Energy

Section 12.2 described the fact that the conservation of momentum in particle interactions is a consequence of the manner in which the underlying elementary waves interact—that the manner in which the waves interact explains why momentum is conserved. Perhaps TEW also explains why the waves interact in just this manner.

The "diffraction" of particles in Chapter 8 provides an example. The angle at which an elementary wave incident on the single-crystal will scatter, in accordance with Bragg's law, depends on the spacing between the planes of atoms in the crystal. Waves actually scatter in all directions off individual atoms in the crystal, but in most directions the waves scattering off one atom interfere destructively with the waves scattering off other atoms, resulting in no net wave leaving the crystal. Only in the direction determined by the Bragg condition will the waves that have scattered everywhere in the crystal add together coherently to produce a net wave leaving the crystal.

As a result, when a particle approaches the single-crystal, it will necessarily be following a wave that has scattered in keeping with the Bragg condition. No other waves will have sufficient amplitude to cause the particle to follow one of them instead. The particle will then scatter at the Bragg-determined angle in following the Bragg-scattered wave.

When a particle scatters, it does so by emitting/absorbing a photon that is absorbed/emitted by the crystal. The wavelength of the elementary wave that the photon follows will be equal to the spacing between the planes in the crystal. So, the spacing of the planes determines both the wavelength of the photon and the angle at which the particle scatters. If one defines the momentum of both the photon and the scattering particle using the by-now-familiar formula $p = h/\lambda$, the resulting photon momentum and particle momentum, along with the scattering angle determined by the Bragg condition, are such that momentum is precisely conserved when the particle scatters.

"Recoil" from emitting or absorbing the photon is not what causes the particle to scatter as it does. Nor does the particle scatter as it does because the individual waves necessarily scatter at that angle. Individual elementary waves scatter at all angles off atoms in the crystal. Momentum is conserved because the scattering particle, as it approaches the crystal, never encounters any waves that would cause it to scatter in any other manner. Conservation of momentum is thereby explained, at least in this particular case, as resulting from nothing more complicated than ordinary wave interference. Destructive interference between waves that scatter in the "wrong" directions leaves particles no avenue to scatter by anything other than the "correct," momentum-conserving angle.

Something very similar is probably what occurs when two otherwise free, charged particles collide and scatter. The interaction of a charged particle with passing photon elementary waves serves to organizes those waves. The resulting organized photon waves act on the elementary waves of a second particle in much the same manner as do the series of planes of atoms in the single-crystal when they scatter an elementary wave. Figure 13.1 illustrates how this organized photon wave might appear. The crests or other features of the photon waves take the place of the planes of atoms. The rest of the analysis is then the same as for the single-crystal scattering. The scattering conserves momentum because the incoming second particle sees only waves that have scattered in a manner that will cause the particle scattering to conserve momentum when the collision occurs.

Perhaps all particle interactions conserve momentum according to this same pattern, thus explaining the classical law of conservation of momentum. It is a quick step from this idea to treat a collision relativistically, in which case this same analysis would explain the classical law of conservation of energy.

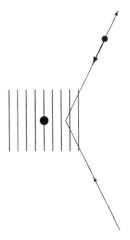

Figure 13.1: "Diffraction" scattering of charged particle

13.3 Subatomic Particle Transformations

When subatomic particles collide, they can transform into entirely different particles. An example of this is illustrated in Figure 11.1, where a collision between a π^- meson and a proton produces a K^0 meson and a Λ^0 particle.

Modern physicists, using quantum mechanics, have obtained some success in developing formulas that correctly predict the probability of such transformations, based on a picture in which only the wave "part" of each "wave-particle" is involved in the interactions. It is likely, then, that interactions between elementary waves, not interactions directly between the particles, cause the transformations to occur as they do. It is equally likely that many of the differences between different kinds of particles are the result more of differences in the waves they follow than of differences in the "innards" of the particles themselves.

In the picture of the universe presented by TEW thus far, elementary waves corresponding to every different kind of particle would have to be everywhere in space at all times. Although there is no valid reason why this could not be the case, it seems much more likely, given the available evidence, that the various different waves corresponding to different particles are combinations or compounds of a set of a few waves—a set of the most elementary elementary-waves.

If elementary waves are indeed such compounds, it stands to reason that interactions between waves might rearrange the components of the compounds, thus explaining the transformation of the particles that would follow those waves. It would be the wave combinations, not the particles per se, that transform.

During the first half of the 20th century, physicists observed many relationships between the wavelengths of the light emitted by atoms when they decay. Physicists used these relationships—as best they could within the confines of quantum mechanics—to piece together the structure of the atom. Modern physicists have similarly observed many relationships between particles, such as relationships between the masses of different particles. But no one has attempted to use those relationships to discover anything about the structure of elementary particles or their waves. Part of the fault for this failure lies in quantum mechanics, which, as indicated in Chapter 5, proclaims that the existence of any such structure would violate the uncertainty principle. But TEW has shown those conclusions of quantum mechanics to be erroneous. Perhaps we can now use the many particle relationships to piece together what the most elementary elementary-waves are and how they combine with one another. We would then be using the relationships to learn more about particles instead of merely combining them into more complicated formulas and using the results to fill libraries, as subatomic particle physicists have been doing for the past fifty-plus years.

Even with those libraries full of formulas, we know nothing more today about the inner structure of particles than we knew fifty years ago. By merely combining formulas without connecting those formulas to anything real, physicists have no basis upon which to use those formulas to determine the structure of anything. By basing their research on quantum mechanics, they have not merely been shooting in the dark, they have been shooting with unreal bullets: the "fields."

TEW provides the basis for finally doing some real research on subatomic particles.

13.4 General Relativity/Gravity

The majority of modern physicists claim that Einstein's so-called "general" theory of relativity explains[1] gravity. Just as in the "special" theory of relativity, described in Chapter 7, these physicists view—at least implicitly—space and time as being some sort of real "stuff." That stuff doesn't merely expand and shrink, as the special theory claims; it can also be curved.

In the earlier Newtonian theory of gravity, a massive body emits a gravitational "field." That field then acts on other massive bodies and produces the gravitational force. The force of gravity that we, as human beings, experience is thus attributed to an alleged gravitational field produced by the earth.

According to general relativity, a massive body does not emit a gravitational field but instead acts—by some unspecified means—to curve space-time. So, for example, when one individual throws a ball to another, we only think the ball follows a curved, or arched, path. General relativity says that the ball is actually traveling on a straight line but in a curved, 4-dimensional space-time. When human beings feel the force of gravity, what is allegedly actually taking place is that the space-time curvature would, if unimpeded, cause us to follow a similar curved path, down into the earth; but the surface of the earth prevents us from doing so. We are thus pushed against the earth's surface, which we experience as gravity. The force that we feel in this manner is analogous to the force that a car door exerts on a passenger when the car turns a corner.

As discussed in Chapter 7, the notion of space, or of space-time, as being some sort of real stuff is absurd. Again: Space and time are *concepts* formed through observation of real objects; they are not real objects themselves.

With TEW, however, we now have something real that can be curved: the elementary waves. Just as in the case of the special theory, perhaps Einstein's general relativity equations do correspond to what

---

[1] Most modern physicists, if asked, would claim that general relativity merely describes gravity as opposed to explaining it; but, in keeping with the "somersault methodology" described in earlier chapters, most physicists go back and forth on this issue.

actually exists, but with curved elementary waves taking the place of the alleged curved space-time.

I have yet to understand a mechanism by which a massive body might produce curvature in the elementary waves. A major "piece" in the explanation of gravity remains to be discovered.

If this TEW picture of gravity is correct, it would resolve one major issue arising from general relativity. In its Einsteinian form, general relativity is a "classical" and not a quantum mechanical theory. It does not involve any wave-particles or the equivalent. Richard Feynman, among others, has argued[2] that a classical theory of gravity is incompatible with a quantum mechanical theory of the motion of the particles affected by that gravity. TEW would resolve this trivially: Elementary waves are "classical." That, in essence, is why TEW works—without the quotation marks—whereas quantum mechanics does not.

---

[2] Richard P. Feynman, *Feynman Lectures on Gravitation*, Westview Press (2003), p. 10ff.